# *Devotional* ADVENTURES FOR KIDS

**Writer**
Marilyn Schneider

**Artist**
Glenn Tower and Cheryl Whelan

Unless otherwise marked, references are taken from the HOLY BIBLE,
NEW INTERNATIONAL VERSION. © 1973, 1978, 1984 International Bible Society.
Used with permission of Zondervan Bible Publishers.

© 1991 Pioneer Clubs®
Box 788, Wheaton, Illinois 60189-0788

This edition published 1993 by The Standard Publishing Company
8121 Hamilton Avenue, Cincinnati, Ohio 45231
Division of Standex International Corporation
All rights reserved. Printed in U.S.A.
ISBN 0-7847-0083-4

STANDARD
PUBLISHING
Cincinnati, Ohio

**1**   ☐ **Pray.** ☐ **Read Genesis 1:1-8.** ☐ **Think about what you read using the three keys on the inside front cover.**

Match the phrases to what God created on the first and second days.

1. What was formless and empty in the beginning     a. night
2. What God called the light     b. sky or heaven
3. What God called the darkness     c. water
4. What God separated     d. earth
5. What God called the area above the water     e. day

**2**   ☐ **Pray.** ☐ **Read Genesis 1:9-19.** ☐ **Think about what you read using the three keys on the inside front cover.**

Follow the lines from the days of creation to the boxes. Then, in each box, draw two more things God created that day.

**3**   ☐ **Pray.** ☐ **Read Genesis 1:20-25.** ☐ **Think about what you read using the three keys on the inside front cover.**

Find out what God did after he blessed the sea creatures and birds. Follow the words through the maze to the earth.

**4**   ☐ **Pray.** ☐ **Read Genesis 1:26-28.** ☐ **Think about what you read using the three keys on the inside front cover.**

Hold your book up to a mirror to translate the backwards message and see how God created human beings.

**5** ☐ **Pray.** ☐ **Read Genesis 1:29-2:3.** ☐ **Think about what you read using the three keys on the inside front cover.**
Use the code to learn what God did on the sixth day of creation.

| A | D | E | G | H | I | L | M | N | O | R | S | T | W | V | Y |
|---|---|---|---|---|---|---|---|---|---|---|---|---|---|---|---|

_____ _____ _____   _____ _____ _____   _____ _____ _____   _____ _____

_____ _____ _____   _____ _____ _____ _____   _____ _____ _____   _____ _____ ,

_____ _____ _____   _____ _____ _____ _____   _____ _____ _____ _____ .

▶ ☐ **Weekend Review**
Recite your memory verse to an adult. In your notebook, list three ways to take care of God's creation (such as collect cans, feed birds). Do one this week.

## WEEK 2          ☐ Memorize: Genesis 3:23

**1** ☐ **Pray.** ☐ **Read Genesis 3:1-5.** ☐ **Think about what you read using the three keys on the inside front cover.**
Black out all the Xs to show the lie the serpent told Eve.

X Y O X X U W X I X X L X X L N O X X T
S U X X R E X L X X Y X X D X I X X E

**2** ☐ **Pray.** ☐ **Read Genesis 3:6-13.** ☐ **Think about what you read using the three keys on the inside front cover.**
Number the following events so they are in the correct order.

_____ Adam and Eve's eyes were opened.
_____ Adam and Eve heard God walking in the garden.
_____ Adam ate the forbidden fruit.
_____ God called to Adam.
_____ Adam blamed Eve.
_____ Eve ate the forbidden fruit.
_____ Eve blamed the serpent.
_____ Eve gave the forbidden fruit to Adam.
_____ Adam and Eve hid from God among the trees.
_____ Adam and Eve sewed fig leaves together for clothes.

**3** ☐ **Pray.** ☐ **Read Genesis 3:14-16.** ☐ **Think about what you read using the three keys on the inside front cover.**

Discover the name of the person who God said would crush the serpent's head. Shade in all the sections of the puzzle marked with an X.

**4** ☐ **Pray.** ☐ **Read Genesis 3:17-19.** ☐ **Think about what you read using the three keys on the inside front cover.**

Find 12 things God named when he told Adam what would happen because of his sin. Look for the listed words across, down, backwards, and diagonally.

| | | | | | | | | | | | | | |
|---|---|---|---|---|---|---|---|---|---|---|---|---|---|
| ground | toil | P | R | O | O | F | I | R | E | B | A | N | D | S |
| days | life | D | A | Y | S | I | N | O | R | A | L | O | T | U |
| thorns | thistles | E | L | O | C | E | Z | O | O | K | R | O | H | N |
| plants | field | N | I | U | H | L | W | M | T | E | I | N | I | R |
| sweat | brow | S | F | O | O | D | N | U | O | R | G | A | S | E |
| food | dust | T | E | N | O | U | T | D | I | S | O | N | T | P |
| | | N | A | I | L | A | W | S | L | A | D | E | L | A |
| | | A | B | L | E | I | C | E | E | T | I | U | E | P |
| | | L | O | W | I | N | T | E | R | A | F | T | S | O |
| | | P | S | U | E | K | A | N | S | N | R | O | H | T |

**5** ☐ **Pray.** ☐ **Read Genesis 3:20-24.** ☐ **Think about what you read using the three keys on the inside front cover.**

Mark the following statements *T* for true or *F* for false.

_____ God made clothes of fig leaves for Adam and Eve.

_____ God said that man knew both good and evil.

_____ God banished Adam and Eve from the Garden of Eden.

_____ Adam had to work the ground in the Garden of Eden.

_____ God put an angel to guard the way to the tree of life.

_____ The angel had a flaming whip.

▶ ☐ **Weekend Review**

Recite your memory verse to an adult. Choose three ways to obey God this week (such as tell the truth or obey your parents). Write them in your notebook.

## WEEK 3    ☐ Memorize: Genesis 15:6

**1** ☐ **Pray.** ☐ **Read Genesis 12:1-9.** ☐ **Think about what you read using the three keys on the inside front cover.**
Cross out the *G*s to see what happened after God told Abram to leave his country.

GAgbragm,Sagragig,Logt,tghegirpogssgessgigongsgangdgpegopleglegfgt fogrCangagang.

**2** ☐ **Pray.** ☐ **Read Genesis 15:1-11.** ☐ **Think about what you read using the three keys on the inside front cover.**
Circle the correct word in each pair to show what God told Abram.

"Don't be **shy/afraid.** I am your **shield/sword**, your very great **helper/reward.**
You will have a **nephew/son** coming from your own **body/family**.
Your **offspring/cattle** will be like the **moon/stars** in the **heavens/earth**."

**3** ☐ **Pray.** ☐ **Read Genesis 15:12-21.** ☐ **Think about what you read using the three keys on the inside front cover.**
Use the code to find out what God promised Abram.

| A | B | C | D | E | F | G | H | I | J | K | L | M | N | O | P | Q | R | S | T | U | V | W | X | Y | Z | space |
|---|---|---|---|---|---|---|---|---|---|---|---|---|---|---|---|---|---|---|---|---|---|---|---|---|---|---|
| 26 | 25 | 24 | 23 | 22 | 21 | 20 | 19 | 18 | 17 | 16 | 15 | 14 | 13 | 12 | 11 | 10 | 9 | 8 | 7 | 6 | 5 | 4 | 3 | 2 | 1 | 0 |

7 12 0 2 12 6 9 0 23 22 8 24 22 13 23 26 13 7 8 0 18 0

_____

20 18 5 22 0 7 19 18 8 0 15 26 13 23

_____

**4** ☐ **Pray.** ☐ **Read Genesis 18:1-8.** ☐ **Think about what you read using the three keys on the inside front cover.**
Solve the puzzle to see how Abraham treated his visitors.

*Across*
1. What Abraham asked Sarah to bake.
3. What Abraham urged them to do under a tree.
7. Abraham brought water to do this.
8. What was washed.

*Down*
2. The man to whom the Lord appeared.
4. What Abraham had his visitors rest under.
5. Abraham hurried from this place to meet them.
6. The meat Abraham had prepared for them.

**5** ☐ **Pray.** ☐ **Read Genesis 18:9-15.** ☐ **Think about what you read using the three keys on the inside front cover.**

Put the sentences in the speech balloons, the Lord's or Sarah's inside the tent.

"You will have a son." "I did not laugh." "Why did you laugh?" "I am too old."

▶ ☐ **Weekend Review**

Recite your memory verse to an adult. Show your love for your family by making a family tree.

## WEEK 4                    ☐ Memorize: Genesis 22:18

**1** ☐ **Pray.** ☐ **Read Genesis 21:1-7.** ☐ **Think about what you read using the three keys on the inside front cover.**

Answer the questions. The circled letters spell the name of a special child.

The Lord did what he had ___ ___ ___ ___ Ⓞ ___ ___ ___ ___.

God brought laughter to Ⓞ ___ ___ ___ ___ ___.

Sarah bore a son for Abraham in his old Ⓞ ___ ___ ___.

The 100-year-old father was ___ ___ ___ Ⓞ ___ ___ ___ ___ ___.

The baby was ___ ___ ___ ___ ___ ___ Ⓞ ___ ___ ___ ___ ___.

**2** ☐ **Pray.** ☐ **Read Genesis 21:8-13.** ☐ **Think about what you read using the three keys on the inside front cover.**

To find out what God said he would make Hagar's son Ishmael into, write the first letter of the object in the box below it.

**3** □ **Pray.** □ **Read Genesis 21:14-20.** □ **Think about what you read using the three keys on the inside front cover.**

Connect the dots to see what God showed Hagar in the desert.

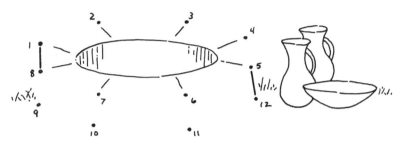

**4** □ **Pray.** □ **Read Genesis 22:1-8.** □ **Think about what you read using the three keys on the inside front cover.**

Learn Abraham's answer to Isaac's question about the sacrifice. In the maze, start with the *G*, and go from letter to letter. Write the letters on the lines.

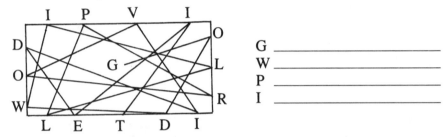

G _____
W _____
P _____
I _____

**5** □ **Pray.** □ **Read Genesis 22:9-19.** □ **Think about what you read using the three keys on the inside front cover.**

Finish the scene to show what happened when Abraham was ready to sacrifice Isaac.

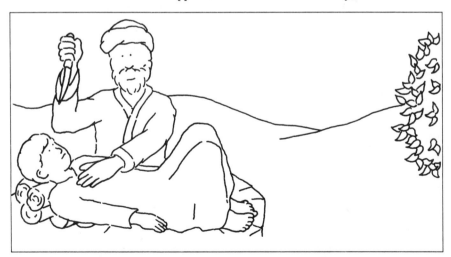

▶ □ **Weekend Review**

Recite your memory verse to an adult. Use a baby name book to find out what your name means. Do the same for your family. Make placecards using the meanings.

**1** ☐ **Pray.** ☐ **Read Matthew 1:18-25.** ☐ **Think about what you read using the three keys on the inside front cover.**

To find out why the baby was to be named Jesus, write in the correct vowels.

| 1 | 2 | 3 | 4 | 5 |
|---|---|---|---|---|
| a | e | i | o | u |

b __ c __ __ s __ h __ w __ l l s __ v __ h __ s
  2    1  5    2    2    3     1  2    3

p __ __ p l __ f r __ m t h __ __ r s __ n s
  2  4   2    4     2  3    3

**2** ☐ **Pray.** ☐ **Read Matthew 2:1-6.** ☐ **Think about what you read using the three keys on the inside front cover.**

The wise men went to two places in Israel. Find the name of the first on the five-pointed stars and the name of the second on the four-pointed stars.

☆ = _____

◆ = _____

**3** ☐ **Pray.** ☐ **Read Matthew 2:7-12.** ☐ **Think about what you read using the three keys on the inside front cover.**

Draw a | box | around the things the wise men did or gave when they found Jesus.

camel    gold    worshipped    silver    sang

myrrh    jewelry    incense    cried    money

**4** ☐ **Pray.** ☐ **Read Matthew 2:13-18.** ☐ **Think about what you read using the three keys on the inside front cover.**

Use the code to learn where and when Jesus' family went.

| D | E | F | G | H | I | L | M | N | O | P | T | Y |
|---|---|---|---|---|---|---|---|---|---|---|---|---|
| ● | ○ | ■ | □ | ▲ | △ | ▼ | ▽ | ◑ | ◐ | ◓ | ⊕ | ⊖ |

⊕ ◑    ○ □ ⊖ ◓ ⊕    △ ◑    ⊕ ▲ ○

▽ △ ● ● ▼ ○    ◑ ■    ⊕ ▲ ○

◑ △ □ ▲ ⊕

**5** □ **Pray.** □ **Read Matthew 2:19-23.** □ **Think about what you read using the three keys on the inside front cover.**

Follow the maze to see where Joseph, Mary, and Jesus went from Egypt to live.

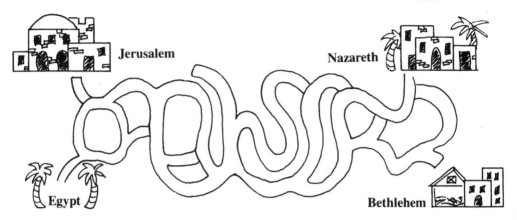

▶ □ **Weekend Review**

Recite your memory verse to an adult. Give a gift of yourself to a friend or family member. Write a note saying what you'll do, such as help, read, or play.

## WEEK 6                                    □ Memorize: Matthew 5:44

**1** □ **Pray.** □ **Read Matthew 5:1-12.** □ **Think about what you read using the three keys on the inside front cover.**

Match the people in the first column with what Jesus said they would receive.

| | |
|---|---|
| The poor in spirit | mercy |
| those who mourn | being called God's sons |
| the meek | comfort |
| the merciful | the kingdom of heaven |
| the pure | seeing God |
| the peacemakers | the earth |

**2** □ **Pray.** □ **Read Matthew 5:13-20.** □ **Think about what you read using the three keys on the inside front cover.**

Shade in the sections marked *N* to uncover what Jesus said Christians should be.

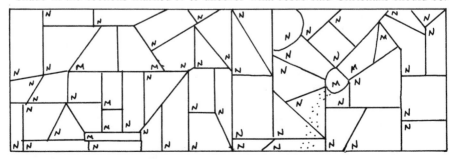

**3** ☐ **Pray.** ☐ **Read Matthew 5:21-26.** ☐ **Think about what you read using the three keys on the inside front cover.**
Circle what Jesus said to do when someone has something against you.

Ignore the problem.

Call the person a fool.

Make peace with the person.

First give a gift to God.

**4** ☐ **Pray.** ☐ **Read Matthew 5:27-37.** ☐ **Think about what you read using the three keys on the inside front cover.**
Go around the wall twice, skipping every other letter, to find out what Jesus said about talking.

START

L A E N T D Y Y O O U U R
S                         R
                          Y
                          N
E
O Y N N N A A E E M M S O E

___ ___ ___ ___ ___

___ ___ ___ ___ ___

**5** ☐ **Pray.** ☐ **Read Matthew 5:38-48.** ☐ **Think about what you read using the three keys on the inside front cover.**
Solve the math problems first. Then look at the code, and put the correct letter under the box to see what Jesus said to do.

| 1 | 2 | 3 | 4 | 5 | 6 | 7 | 8 | 9 | 10 | 11 |
|---|---|---|---|---|---|---|---|---|----|----|
| E | I | L | M | N | O | R | S | U | V | Y |

$$6-3 \quad 4+2 \quad 2+8 \quad 10-9 \qquad 7+4 \quad 8-2 \quad 5+4 \quad 8-1$$

☐ ☐ ☐ ☐   ☐ ☐ ☐ ☐

___ ___ ___ ___   ___ ___ ___ ___

$$9-8 \quad 3+2 \quad 10-9 \quad 9-5 \quad 5-3 \quad 1+0 \quad 3+5$$

☐ ☐ ☐ ☐ ☐ ☐ ☐

___ ___ ___ ___ ___ ___ ___

▶ ☐ **Weekend Review**
Recite your memory verse to an adult. In your notebook, list three ways you can be kind this week. Check them off when you do them.

**1** ☐ **Pray.** ☐ **Read John 3:1-8.** ☐ **Think about what you read using the three keys on the inside front cover.**
Write the words of Nicodemus' question where they belong on the puzzle.

a  can  be  born  when  again  how  old  man

**2** ☐ **Pray.** ☐ **Read John 3:9-15.** ☐ **Think about what you read using the three keys on the inside front cover.**
Search for words from Jesus' reply to Nicodemus.

| | | |
|---|---|---|
| teacher | desert | |
| believe | snake | |
| truth | eternal | |
| Son of Man | life | |
| Moses | testimony | |

```
K L Z E V E I L E B E A D
S J R E H C A E T F A I N
M O S E S N A K E R I M S
A B E N D E S E R T U L O
L T E S T I M O N Y R T M
L Q S O N O F M A N A S H
S K C A B E L T L O N G S
```

**3** ☐ **Pray.** ☐ **Read John 3:16-21.** ☐ **Think about what you read using the three keys on the inside front cover.**
Fill in the broken letters to find out why Jesus was sent to earth.

GOD LOVED THE WORLD

**4** ☐ **Pray.** ☐ **Read John 3:22-30.** ☐ **Think about what you read using the three keys on the inside front cover.**
Cross out the wrong words from the statement John the Baptist made.

I am [not / so] the [Elijah / Christ] but am [sent / going] [behind / ahead] of [him / others]

**5** ☐ **Pray.** ☐ **Read John 3:31-36.** ☐ **Think about what you read using the three keys on the inside front cover.**

Use the code to find out a message about Jesus.

| A | B | E | F | H | I | L | N | O | R | S | T | V | W |
|---|---|---|---|---|---|---|---|---|---|---|---|---|---|
| ☺ | ☺ | ☺ | ☺ | ☺ | ☺ | ☺ | ☺ | ☺ | ☺ | ☺ | ☺ | ☺ | ☺ |

___ ___ ___ ___ ___ ___ ___     ___ ___ ___ ___ ___ ___ ___ ___

___ ___     ___ ___ ___     ___ ___ ___     ___ ___ ___

___ ___ ___ ___ ___ ___ ___     ___ ___ ___ ___

▶ ☐ **Weekend Review**

Recite your memory verse to an adult. In your notebook, make a coded message of what you learned about Jesus this week. Give it to a friend to figure out.

---

## WEEK 8        ☐ Memorize: John 6:48

**1** ☐ **Pray.** ☐ **Read John 6:24-29.** ☐ **Think about what you read using the three keys on the inside front cover.**

Fill in the crossword puzzle with the answers about the crowd and Jesus.

The crowd crossed the __ *(3 Across)*
in __ *(1 Down)* to find __ *(2 Down)*.
He told them to __ *(1 Across)* on
the one God has __ *(4 Across)*.

**2** ☐ **Pray.** ☐ **Read John 6:30-40.** ☐ **Think about what you read using the three keys on the inside front cover.**

Use the sounds of the objects to learn what Jesus said about himself.

___ ___ ___     ___ ___ ___ ___     ___ ___     ___ ___ ___ ___

**3** ☐ **Pray.** ☐ **Read John 6:41-51.** ☐ **Think about what you read using the three keys on the inside front cover.**
Read the message in the correct order to find out what people said about Jesus.

**6** I came down from heaven?

**4** whose parents we know?

**5** How can he say

**1** The people grumbled

**3** the son of Joseph

**2** Isn't this Jesus

**4** ☐ **Pray.** ☐ **Read John 6:52-59.** ☐ **Think about what you read using the three keys on the inside front cover.**
Add the correct vowels to see what Jesus said.

A   △E   ◯I   ☆O   ◆U

J◆S T   ☐S   ◯   L◯v△

B△c☐◆s△   ☆F   TH△   F☐TH△R,

S☆   Y☆◆   W◯L L   L◯v△

B△c☐◆s△   ☆F M△.

**5** ☐ **Pray.** ☐ **Read John 6:60-71.** ☐ **Think about what you read using the three keys on the inside front cover.**
Draw a line from the questions to who asked them.

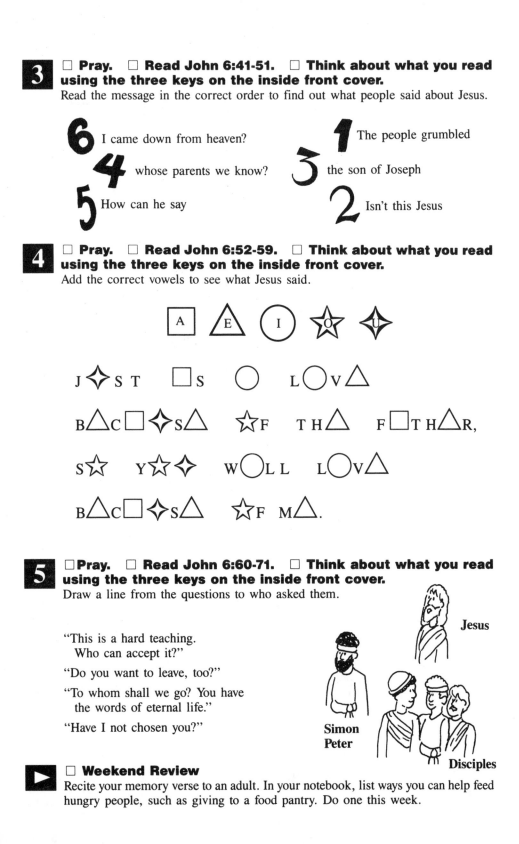

"This is a hard teaching. Who can accept it?"

"Do you want to leave, too?"

"To whom shall we go? You have the words of eternal life."

"Have I not chosen you?"

Jesus

Simon Peter

Disciples

▶ ☐ **Weekend Review**
Recite your memory verse to an adult. In your notebook, list ways you can help feed hungry people, such as giving to a food pantry. Do one this week.

**1** ☐ **Pray.** ☐ **Read Genesis 25:19-26.** ☐ **Think about what you read using the three keys on the inside front cover.**

Write the correct numbers in the statements about Isaac's family.

## 1  **2**  **40**  60

Isaac was _____ years old when he married Rebekah. Rebekah gave birth to _____ boys. God said _____ would serve the other. Isaac was _____ years old when they were born.

**2** ☐ **Pray.** ☐ **Read Genesis 25:27-34.** ☐ **Think about what you read using the three keys on the inside front cover.**

Match the facts to the correct twin brother, Esau or Jacob.

liked the open country
wanted his brother's birthright
loved by Isaac
loved by Rebekah
quiet
skillful hunter
sold his birthright for food
stayed by the tents

Esau                                              Jacob

**3** ☐ **Pray.** ☐ **Read Genesis 27:1-13.** ☐ **Think about what you read using the three keys on the inside front cover.**

Write the first letter of each object to see who planned how to trick Isaac.

____  ____  ____  ____  ____  ____  ____

**4** ☐ **Pray.** ☐ **Read Genesis 27:14-29.** ☐ **Think about what you read using the three keys on the inside front cover.**

In the boxes, write Isaac's questions and Jacob's lies in the correct order.

| *Questions* | *Answers* |
|---|---|
| Who is it? | I am. |
| Are you really Esau? | The Lord gave me success. |
| How did you find game so quickly? | I am Esau, your firstborn. |

| Isaac | Jacob | Isaac | Jacob | Isaac | Jacob |
|---|---|---|---|---|---|
| | | | | | |

**5** ☐ **Pray.** ☐ **Read Genesis 27:30-40.** ☐ **Think about what you read using the three keys on the inside front cover.**
Black out the upside-down teardrops to see what Esau cried to his father.

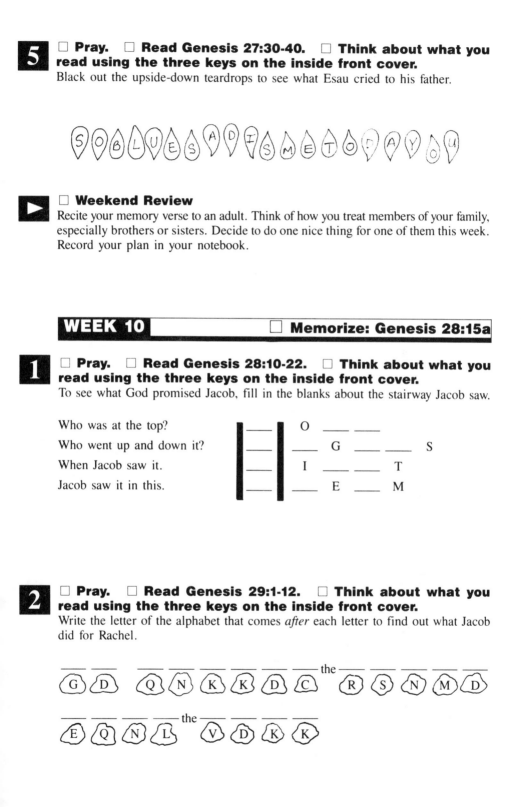

▶ ☐ **Weekend Review**
Recite your memory verse to an adult. Think of how you treat members of your family, especially brothers or sisters. Decide to do one nice thing for one of them this week. Record your plan in your notebook.

## WEEK 10 ☐ Memorize: Genesis 28:15a

**1** ☐ **Pray.** ☐ **Read Genesis 28:10-22.** ☐ **Think about what you read using the three keys on the inside front cover.**
To see what God promised Jacob, fill in the blanks about the stairway Jacob saw.

Who was at the top?
Who went up and down it?
When Jacob saw it.
Jacob saw it in this.

```
___ | O ___ ___
___ | ___ G ___ ___ S
___ | I ___ ___ T
___ | ___ E ___ M
```

**2** ☐ **Pray.** ☐ **Read Genesis 29:1-12.** ☐ **Think about what you read using the three keys on the inside front cover.**
Write the letter of the alphabet that comes *after* each letter to find out what Jacob did for Rachel.

___ ___  ___ ___ ___ ___ ___ ___ —the— ___ ___ ___ ___ ___
G D  Q N K K D C  R S N M D

___ ___ ___ ___ —the— ___ ___ ___ ___
E Q N L  V D K K

**3** ☐ **Pray.** ☐ **Read Genesis 29:13-20.** ☐ **Think about what you read using the three keys on the inside front cover.**

Use the code to find out why Jacob worked seven years for Laban.

| A | C | D | E | H | L | O | R | V |
|---|---|---|---|---|---|---|---|---|
| ♡ | ♡ | ♡ | ♥ | ♡ | ♡ | ♥ | ♡ | ♡ |

♥ ♥   ♡ ♥ ♡ ♥ ♡   ♡ ♡ ♡ ♥ ♥ ♥

___ ___   ___ ___ ___ ___ ___   ___ ___ ___ ___ ___ ___

**4** ☐ **Pray.** ☐ **Read Genesis 29:21-30.** ☐ **Think about what you read using the three keys on the inside front cover.**

Do the math problems first, and then write in the correct letter to see why Jacob worked seven more years for Laban.

| 3 | 4 | 5 | 6 | 7 |
|---|---|---|---|---|
| A | E | I | O | Y |

$$\begin{array}{cc} 7 \\ -4 \end{array} \quad \begin{array}{cc} 10 \\ -7 \end{array} \qquad \begin{array}{cc} 7 \\ -2 \end{array} \qquad \begin{array}{cc} 11 \\ -7 \end{array} \qquad \begin{array}{cc} 7 \\ -2 \end{array}$$

☐ ☐     ☐     ☐     ☐

L ___ B ___ N   T R ___ C K ___ D   H ___ M

$$\begin{array}{cc} 12 \\ -7 \end{array} \quad \begin{array}{cc} 7 \\ -1 \end{array} \quad \begin{array}{cc} 7 \\ -4 \end{array} \quad \begin{array}{cc} 7 \\ -0 \end{array} \begin{array}{cc} 7 \\ -2 \end{array} \quad \begin{array}{cc} 7 \\ -3 \end{array} \begin{array}{cc} 10 \\ -7 \end{array}$$

☐ ☐   ☐   ☐ ☐   ☐ ☐

___ N T ___   M ___ R R ___   ___ N G   L ___ ___ H

**5** ☐ **Pray.** ☐ **Read Genesis 29:31-36; 30:22-24.** ☐ **Think about what you read using the three keys on the inside front cover.**

Mark the statements about Leah and Rachel *True* or *False*.

____ God saw Leah was not loved.     ____ Leah had only one son.

____ God gave Leah children.     ____ God listened to Rachel.

____ Reuben was born to Rachel.     ____ Joseph was born to Leah.

▶ ☐ **Weekend Review**

Recite your memory verse to an adult. In your notebook, make a word search puzzle of things God has promised you, such as to love you and care for you. Give it to a friend to do.

**1** ☐ **Pray.** ☐ **Read Genesis 37:1-11.** ☐ **Think about what you read using the three keys on the inside front cover.**
Find the letters of the name of Jacob's favorite son hidden in the pictures.

**2** ☐ **Pray.** ☐ **Read Genesis 37:12-24.** ☐ **Think about what you read using the three keys on the inside front cover.**
Number the statements about Joseph and his brothers in the correct order.

_____ Joseph's brothers plotted to kill him.

_____ Joseph's brothers said, "Here comes that dreamer!"

_____ Joseph's brothers stripped off his beautiful robe.

_____ Joseph's brothers took their flocks to Sechem.

_____ Joseph's brothers threw him in an empty pit.

_____ Reuben said, "Let's not kill him."

_____ Joseph's father sent him to find his brothers.

**3** ☐ **Pray.** ☐ **Read Genesis 37:25-36.** ☐ **Think about what you read using the three keys on the inside front cover.**
Cross out the Qs to see what Joseph's brothers showed their father, Jacob.

J Q O S Q E P H Q S Q C O Q A T Q D Q I P P Q E Q D Q

Q I N Q Q B Q L Q O O Q Q D

**4** ☐ **Pray.** ☐ **Read Genesis 39:1-10.** ☐ **Think about what you read using the three keys on the inside front cover.**
Follow the maze to show where Joseph went in Egypt.

START➔

Potiphar's House

Desert

Pyramids   Pharaoh's Palace

**5** ☐ **Pray.** ☐ **Read Genesis 39:11-23.** ☐ **Think about what you read using the three keys on the inside front cover.**

Use the code to see what Joseph told Potiphar's wife when she tempted him.

| A | B | C | | L | N | O |
|---|---|---|---|---|---|---|
| **D** | **E** | **G** | | **S** | **T** | **U** |
| **H** | **I** | **K** | | **V** | **W** | **X** |

• = space

*(coded message in pigpen cipher)*

▶ ☐ **Weekend Review**

Recite your memory verse to an adult. In your notebook, list ways to help a refugee family or someone new to your school or neighborhood. Choose one to do this week.

## WEEK 12 ☐ Memorize: Genesis 41:39

**1** ☐ **Pray.** ☐ **Read Genesis 40:1-14.** ☐ **Think about what you read using the three keys on the inside front cover.**

Use the code to find out how Joseph could interpret dreams in prison.

*(picture code key)* A E I O

G_D G_V_ H__M TH_ _NT_RPR_T_T__NS

**2** ☐ **Pray.** ☐ **Read Genesis 41:15-16, 25-35.** ☐ **Think about what you read using the three keys on the inside front cover.**

Use the pictures to show what Joseph said Pharaoh's dream meant.

| | | |
|---|---|---|
| *(cows)* | 7 healthy cows | 7 thin heads of grain *(grain)* |
| *(cows)* | 7 thin cows | 7 years of plenty ☺ |
| *(grain)* | 7 good heads of grain | 7 years of famine ☹ |

*(cow)* ¢ = ◯

¢ *(grain)* = ◯

**3** ☐ **Pray.** ☐ **Read Genesis 41:37-49, 53-57.** ☐ **Think about what you read using the three keys on the inside front cover.**
Look up, down, forwards, backwards to find the things Pharaoh gave Joseph.

power

ring

new name

linen robes

gold chain

chariot

wife Asenath

| W | H | R | B | S | E | B | O | R | N | E | N | I | L | I |
|---|---|---|---|---|---|---|---|---|---|---|---|---|---|---|
| A | A | L | G | O | L | D | C | H | A | I | N | B | S | V |
| K | R | Q | N | N | E | W | N | A | M | E | Z | J | R | U |
| O | Z | W | I | F | E | A | S | E | N | A | T | H | Y | D |
| T | O | I | R | A | H | C | N | B | L | R | E | W | O | P |

**4** ☐ **Pray.** ☐ **Read Genesis 42:1-12.** ☐ **Think about what you read using the three keys on the inside front cover.**
To find out what Jacob told his sons, skip every other letter.

START→ I G V O E D H O E W A N I W N O I S A A U P G N R Y S T O H T E H R E E R A E N D S C B G U R Y A S E O G E O G R Y U P S T

**5** ☐ **Pray.** ☐ **Read Genesis 42:13-26.** ☐ **Think about what you read using the three keys on the inside front cover.**
To see what Joseph's brothers said when they had trouble in Egypt, choose the correct word in every pair.

"We are being **rewarded/punished** because of our **brother/father.** We **saw/heard** how **happy/distressed** he was when he **pleaded/yelled** with **them/us** for his **money/life,** but we would not **listen/help.**"

▶ ☐ **Weekend Review**
Recite your memory verse to an adult. In your notebook, list three ways you can tell others about the things they do well. This week, pick three people you know and tell them what you like about them.

**1**  ☐ **Pray.**  ☐ **Read Genesis 43:1-14.**  ☐ **Think about what you read using the three keys on the inside front cover.**
Shade in the spaces with Xs to show who Judah promised to look out for.

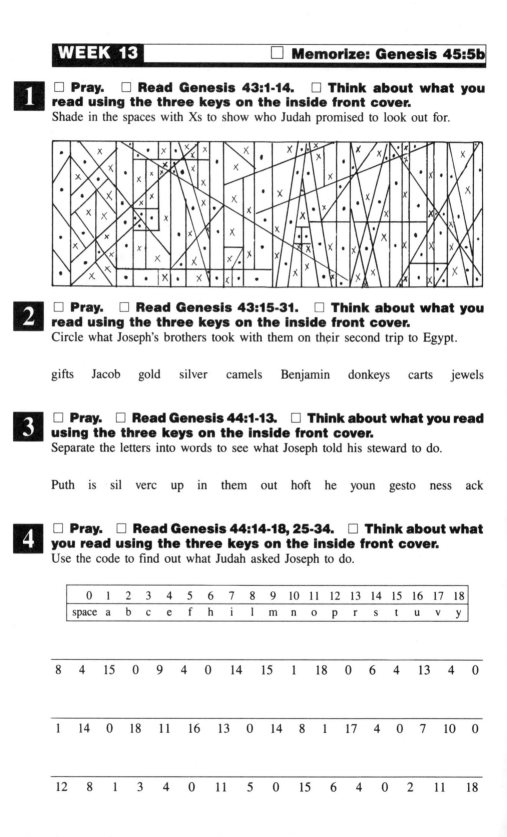

**2**  ☐ **Pray.**  ☐ **Read Genesis 43:15-31.**  ☐ **Think about what you read using the three keys on the inside front cover.**
Circle what Joseph's brothers took with them on their second trip to Egypt.

gifts   Jacob   gold   silver   camels   Benjamin   donkeys   carts   jewels

**3**  ☐ **Pray.**  ☐ **Read Genesis 44:1-13.**  ☐ **Think about what you read using the three keys on the inside front cover.**
Separate the letters into words to see what Joseph told his steward to do.

Puth   is   sil   verc   up   in   them   out   hoft   he   youn   gesto   ness   ack

**4**  ☐ **Pray.**  ☐ **Read Genesis 44:14-18, 25-34.**  ☐ **Think about what you read using the three keys on the inside front cover.**
Use the code to find out what Judah asked Joseph to do.

| 0 | 1 | 2 | 3 | 4 | 5 | 6 | 7 | 8 | 9 | 10 | 11 | 12 | 13 | 14 | 15 | 16 | 17 | 18 |
|---|---|---|---|---|---|---|---|---|---|----|----|----|----|----|----|----|----|----|
| space | a | b | c | e | f | h | i | l | m | n | o | p | r | s | t | u | v | y |

8  4  15  0  9  4  0  14  15  1  18  0  6  4  13  4  0

1  14  0  18  11  16  13  0  14  8  1  17  4  0  7  10  0

12  8  1  3  4  0  11  5  0  15  6  4  0  2  11  18

**5** ☐ **Pray.** ☐ **Read Genesis 45:1-15.** ☐ **Think about what you read using the three keys on the inside front cover.**

Fill in the letters from the code to see what Joseph told his brothers.

| D | F | G | H | L | M | N | R | S | T | V | Y |
|---|---|---|---|---|---|---|---|---|---|---|---|
| ◎ | ∩ | △ | □ | ‖ | ◉ | ⊐ | ◬ | ▣ | Γ | ∪ | ☰ |

△ _ o ◎ _ ▣ _ _ e ⊐ Γ _ ◉ _ e _ ▣ _ a _ e a _ ◎ _ o ∩

☰ _ o u Γ _ o ▣ _ a ∪ _ e ☰ _ o ◬ ‖ ∪ i ▣ _ e

☐ **Weekend Review**

Recite your memory verse to an adult. In your notebook, draw a cartoon about a time someone treated you badly and how God can turn it into something good.

**WEEK 14** ☐ **Memorize: Matthew 8:27b**

**1** ☐ **Pray.** ☐ **Read Matthew 8:5-13.** ☐ **Think about what you read using the three keys on the inside front cover.**

Read the sentence from right to left to see what Jesus said about the centurion.

faith great such with Israel in anyone found not have I

**2** ☐ **Pray.** ☐ **Read Matthew 8:14-22.** ☐ **Think about what you read using the three keys on the inside front cover.**

Use the pictures and their sounds to find out what Jesus said about himself.

-i +a   +h -bw   and

-i +a   +s   but the

of   has

**3** ☐ **Pray.** ☐ **Read Matthew 8:23-27.** ☐ **Think about what you read using the three keys on the inside front cover.**

Read across the waves to see what the disciples said about Jesus after the storm.

what kind of MAN IS THIS? EVEN the wind And the waves obey him!

**4** ☐ **Pray.** ☐ **Read Matthew 8:28-34.** ☐ **Think about what you read using the three keys on the inside front cover.**

Put the answers in the puzzle about what happened in the Gadarene region.

Two _____ (*7 Across*) men met Jesus. They were so _____ (*2 Down*) no one went near them. They shouted, "What do you want with us, _____ (*6 Across*)?" The demons _____ (*9 Across*) Jesus to send them into a _____ (*3 Down*) of _____ (*8 Down*). Then they rushed down a steep _____ (*9 Down*) into the _____ (*10 Across*) and died in the _____ (*5 Down*). The whole _____ (*4 Down*) asked Jesus to _____ (*1 Across*).

**5** ☐ **Pray.** ☐ **Read Matthew 9:1-8.** ☐ **Think about what you read using the three keys on the inside front cover.**

Use the code to find out why Jesus healed the paralytic man.

| a | e | i | o | u | w | y | space |
|---|---|---|---|---|---|---|---|
| ◑ | ◐ | ◖ | ◗ | ◒ | ◣ | ● | ○ |

T◖◗ s h◖◐○h◐○h◐○h◐ s○◐◒th◖ r◖ t●○◖n

○◐◐r t h○t◖○ f◖r g◖v◐○s ◖n s

**▶** ☐ **Weekend Review**

Recite your memory verse to an adult. Pick a tune you like, and write a song about Jesus to fit it. Or put the memory verse to music. Sing it to someone.

**1** ☐ **Pray.** ☐ **Read Mark 5:21-24.** ☐ **Think about what you read using the three keys on the inside front cover.**

Read the words in the letters to see what Jairus asked Jesus about his daughter.

P(LEASE) H(EAL) H(ER) S(O) S(HE) W(ILL) L(IVE)

**2** ☐ **Pray.** ☐ **Read Mark 5:25-34.** ☐ **Think about what you read using the three keys on the inside front cover.**

Number the statements in the correct order.

_____ Jesus felt power go out of him.

_____ Jesus kept looking around.

_____ A woman came up behind Jesus in the crowd and touched his cloak.

_____ His disciples said there were too many people to know who did it.

_____ The woman fell at Jesus' feet and told him what she did.

_____ Jesus said, "Your faith has healed you. Go in peace."

_____ The woman's bleeding stopped immediately.

_____ Jesus stopped and asked, "Who touched my clothes?"

**3** ☐ **Pray.** ☐ **Read Mark 5:35-43.** ☐ **Think about what you read using the three keys on the inside front cover.**

Cross out the Ws to see what Jesus told Jairus when people said his daughter was dead.

DWONWTWWBWEAWFRWAIWD; WJWUWSTWBWEWLIEWVWE.

**4** ☐ **Pray.** ☐ **Read Mark 6:1-6.** ☐ **Think about what you read using the three keys on the inside front cover.**

Use the code to find out how Jesus felt in his home town.

| a | e | i | o |
|---|---|---|---|

H__ w__s __m__z__d __t th__ __r

l__ck __f f__ __th.

**5** ☐ **Pray.** ☐ **Read Mark 6:7-13.** ☐ **Think about what you read using the three keys on the inside front cover.**
Follow the maze through what Jesus told his disciples to take or what they did.

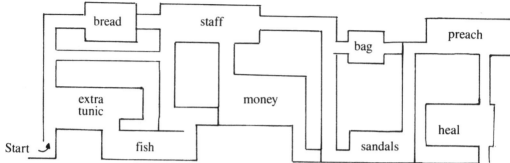

Finish

**▶** ☐ **Weekend Review**
Recite your memory verse to an adult. In your notebook, list ways to cheer up a sick person, such as sending a card or visiting. The next time a friend or family member is sick, do one of these things.

## WEEK 16                              ☐ Memorize: Luke 9:25

**1** ☐ **Pray.** ☐ **Read Luke 9:10-17.** ☐ **Think about what you read using the three keys on the inside front cover.**
Put the correct numbers in the sentences about the miracle Jesus did.

# 2  5  12  **12**  50  5,000

With ☐ loaves and ☐ fish, Jesus fed ☐ men. The people sat in groups of ☐.
Afterwards, the ☐ disciples picked up ☐ basketfuls of leftover food.

**2** ☐ **Pray.** ☐ **Read Luke 9:18-27.** ☐ **Think about what you read using the three keys on the inside front cover.**
Put Jesus' questions and the disciples answers in the correct speech balloons.

"John the Baptist"  "Who do people say I am?"  "One of the prophets"  "Elijah"
"The Christ of God"  "Who do you say I am?"

**3** □ **Pray.** □ **Read Luke 9:28-36.** □ **Think about what you read using the three keys on the inside front cover.**

Follow the arrows to find out what the voice in the cloud said about Jesus.

**4** □ **Pray.** □ **Read Luke 9:37-45.** □ **Think about what you read using the three keys on the inside front cover.**

Use the code to see how the crowd felt when Jesus healed the boy with the evil spirit.

| + | * | – | ⟨ | ⟩ | # | % | • | / | = | ≠ | ÷ | × | ♭ | ♩ | √ | ° |
|---|---|---|---|---|---|---|---|---|---|---|---|---|---|---|---|---|
| A | D | E | F | G | H | L | M | N | O | R | S | T | W | Y | Z | space |

× # – ♩ ° ♭ – ≠ – ° + % % ° + • + √ – * ° + × ° × # – °

_____

⟩ ≠ – + × / – ÷ ÷ ° = ⟨ ° ⟩ = *

_____

**5** □ **Pray.** □ **Read Luke 9:46-50.** □ **Think about what you read using the three keys on the inside front cover.**

Put the correct letters in the statement Jesus made when his disciples argued.

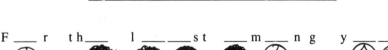

F __ r  t h __  l __ __ s t  __ m __ n g  y __ __

__ l l  __ s  t h __  g r __ __ t __ s t

▶ □ **Weekend Review**

Recite your memory verse to an adult. Think about who you think Jesus is. Write it in your notebook, and then talk with an adult about it.

**1** ☐ Pray. ☐ Read Luke 15:1-7. ☐ Think about what you read using the three keys on the inside front cover.

Follow the words in the maze to see what Jesus said a person who lost one sheep would do.

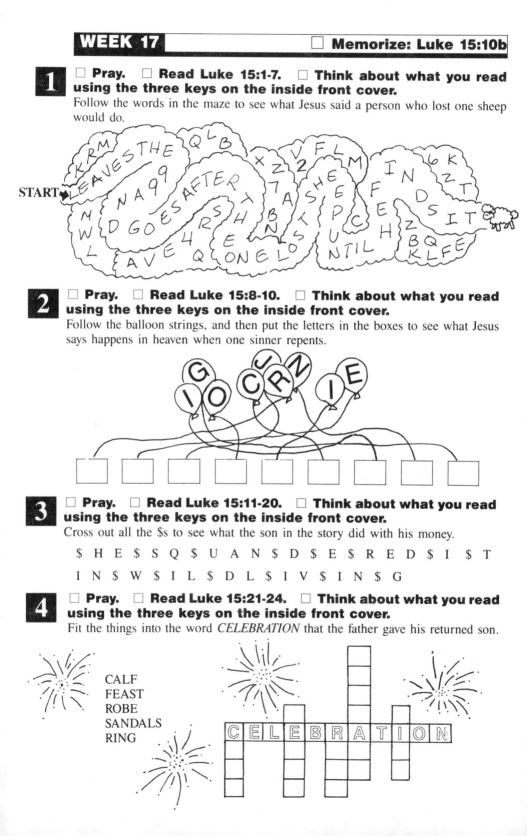

**2** ☐ Pray. ☐ Read Luke 15:8-10. ☐ Think about what you read using the three keys on the inside front cover.

Follow the balloon strings, and then put the letters in the boxes to see what Jesus says happens in heaven when one sinner repents.

**3** ☐ Pray. ☐ Read Luke 15:11-20. ☐ Think about what you read using the three keys on the inside front cover.

Cross out all the $s to see what the son in the story did with his money.

$ H E $ S Q $ U A N $ D $ E $ R E D $ I $ T

I N $ W $ I L $ D L $ I V $ I N $ G

**4** ☐ Pray. ☐ Read Luke 15:21-24. ☐ Think about what you read using the three keys on the inside front cover.

Fit the things into the word *CELEBRATION* that the father gave his returned son.

CALF
FEAST
ROBE
SANDALS
RING

C E L E B R A T I O N

**5** ☐ **Pray.** ☐ **Read Luke 15:25-32.** ☐ **Think about what you read using the three keys on the inside front cover.**
Cross out the wrong words in what the father explained to his unhappy older son.

We had to **cry/celebrate** and be **glad/sad** because your **uncle/brother** was **lost/home** and is **rich/found.**

▶ ☐ **Weekend Review**
Recite your memory verse to an adult. Plan a party for your family and friends to celebrate what God has done for them. Record your plan in your notebook.

## WEEK 18       ☐ Memorize: Mark 12:30

**1** ☐ **Pray.** ☐ **Read Mark 12:1-12.** ☐ **Think about what you read using the three keys on the inside front cover.**
Read across the wall, skipping the cracked stones, to see what Psalm Jesus quoted about himself.

| The | way | stone | of | the | workers |
|---|---|---|---|---|---|
| builders | made | did | every | not | only |
| want | to | became | looked | the | very |
| most | least | important | red | one | two |

**2** ☐ **Pray.** ☐ **Read Mark 12:13-17.** ☐ **Think about what you read using the three keys on the inside front cover.**
To see what Jesus said about taxes, read the coins in the order of their worth.

| Caesar's 10 and to | God's 50 | God 25 what is | Give 1 to | Caesar 5 what is |
|---|---|---|---|---|

**3** □ **Pray.** □ **Read Mark 12:18-27.** □ **Think about what you read using the three keys on the inside front cover.**
Use the code to find out what Jesus told the Sadducees about God.

| Z | Y | X | W | V | U | T | S | R | Q | P | O | N | M | L | K | J | I | H | G | F | E | D | C | B | A |
|---|---|---|---|---|---|---|---|---|---|---|---|---|---|---|---|---|---|---|---|---|---|---|---|---|---|
| A | B | C | D | E | F | G | H | I | J | K | L | M | N | O | P | Q | R | S | T | U | V | W | X | Y | Z |

_____

SV RH MLG GSV TLW LU GSV WVZW, YFG

_____

LU GSV ORERMT.

**4** □ **Pray.** □ **Read Mark 12:28-34.** □ **Think about what you read using the three keys on the inside front cover.**
Put the words in their spots to see what Jesus said are the greatest commandments.

Love the Lord your God with all your [_____]
and with all your [_____] and with all your
[_____] and with all your [_____].
Love your [_____] as yourself.

strength   heart   mind   soul   neighbor

**5** □ **Pray.** □ **Read Mark 12:35-44.** □ **Think about what you read using the three keys on the inside front cover.**
Unscramble the words to find out who Jesus said gave the biggest offering.

OPRO   DIWWO _____

▶ □ **Weekend Review**
Recite your memory verse to an adult. Make a plan of how you can give to God, such as with your money or by helping at church. Record the plan in your notebook, and put it into action this week.

**1** ☐ **Pray.** ☐ **Read Joshua 1:1-9.** ☐ **Think about what you read using the three keys on the inside front cover.**
Draw in the correct signs to complete the instructions God gave Joshua.

| TURN | OBEY | LEFT | CAREFUL | RIGHT |
|---|---|---|---|---|

Be ___ to ___ all the law. Don't ___ from it, to the ___ or to the ___ .

**2** ☐ **Pray.** ☐ **Read Joshua 1:10-18.** ☐ **Think about what you read using the three keys on the inside front cover.**
Cross out all the Hs to find out what the people told their new leader, Joshua.

HBHEHSTHROHNGHAHHNDHHCHOUHRHAGHEHOHHUHSH

**3** ☐ **Pray.** ☐ **Read Joshua 2:1-7.** ☐ **Think about what you read using the three keys on the inside front cover.**
Use the sounds of the objects to find out what happened to the men Joshua sent.

(sun) (hat) –t+b (disc) –l+h the (2) s + (pies)

**4** ☐ **Pray.** ☐ **Read Joshua 2:8-14.** ☐ **Think about what you read using the three keys on the inside front cover.**
Use the code to find out what Rahab said to the spies.

| 26 | 25 | 24 | 23 | 22 | 21 | 20 | 19 | 18 | 17 | 16 | 15 | 14 | 13 | 12 | 11 | 10 | 9 | 8 | 7 | 6 | 5 | 4 | 3 | 2 | 1 | 0 |
|---|---|---|---|---|---|---|---|---|---|---|---|---|---|---|---|---|---|---|---|---|---|---|---|---|---|---|
| A | B | C | D | E | F | G | H | I | J | K | L | M | N | O | P | Q | R | S | T | U | V | W | X | Y | Z | space |

18 0 16 13 12 4 0 7 19 26 7 0 7 19 22 0 15 12 9 23 0 19 26 8 0 20 18 5 22 13 0

7 19 18 8 0 15 26 13 23 0 7 12 0 2 12 6 0 26 13 23 0 7 19 26 7 0 26 0 20 9 22 26 7

0 21 22 26 9 0 12 21 0 2 12 6 0 19 26 8 0 21 26 15 15 22 13 0 12 13 0 6 8.

**5** ☐ **Pray.** ☐ **Read Joshua 2:15-24.** ☐ **Think about what you read using the three keys on the inside front cover.**

Follow the line to find out what the spies told Rahab to hang in her window.

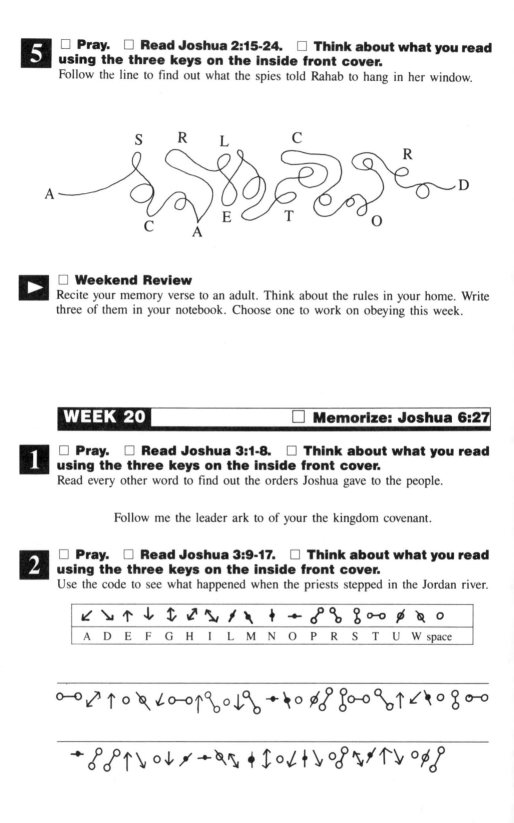

▶ ☐ **Weekend Review**

Recite your memory verse to an adult. Think about the rules in your home. Write three of them in your notebook. Choose one to work on obeying this week.

## WEEK 20 ☐ Memorize: Joshua 6:27

**1** ☐ **Pray.** ☐ **Read Joshua 3:1-8.** ☐ **Think about what you read using the three keys on the inside front cover.**

Read every other word to find out the orders Joshua gave to the people.

Follow me the leader ark to of your the kingdom covenant.

**2** ☐ **Pray.** ☐ **Read Joshua 3:9-17.** ☐ **Think about what you read using the three keys on the inside front cover.**

Use the code to see what happened when the priests stepped in the Jordan river.

| ↙ | ↘ | ↑ | ↓ | ↕ | ↗ | ↘ | ↗ | ↖ | ✝ | ↔ | ⧏⧐ | ⧐⧏ | ⧐○ | ∅ | ⊘ | ○ |
|---|---|---|---|---|---|---|---|---|---|---|---|---|---|---|---|---|
| A | D | E | F | G | H | I | L | M | N | O | P | R | S | T | U | W space |

**3** □ **Pray.** □ **Read Joshua 6:1-11.** □ **Think about what you read using the three keys on the inside front cover.**

Check off the things the Lord told Joshua to do to win the city of Jericho.

□ March around Jericho once for six days.

□ Tell the people to sing as they march.

□ Have seven priests play seven harps.

□ Have the priests carry the ark.

□ March around Jericho twice the seventh day.

□ Have the people be quiet until the signal.

**4** □ **Pray.** □ **Read Joshua 6:12-21.** □ **Think about what you read using the three keys on the inside front cover.**

To see what happened at the trumpet signal, read the boxes marked with circles.

| ○ | □ | ○ | ○ | □ | ○ | □ | ○ | ○ | □ | ○ | □ |
|------|--------|--------|------|------|------|------|------|-------|------|------|------|
| The | priest | people | gave | saw | a | big | loud | shout | at | the | only |

| ○ | ○ | □ | ○ | ○ | □ | ○ | □ | ○ | ○ | □ | ○ |
|------|------|------|------|------|------|------|------|------|------|------|------|
| wall | fell | flat | down | and | all | they | ran | took | the | into | city |

**5** □ **Pray.** □ **Read Joshua 6:22-27.** □ **Think about what you read using the three keys on the inside front cover.**

Fill in the letters to find out who were the only ones saved from Jericho.

RAHAB, HER ENTIRE FAMILY, & ALL WHO BELONGED TO HER

▶ □ **Weekend Review**

Recite your memory verse to an adult. Get several friends together and work as a team to help an older person with jobs around the house, such as raking leaves.

**1** ☐ **Pray.** ☐ **Read Ruth 1:1-7.** ☐ **Think about what you read using the three keys on the inside front cover.**
Unscramble the words to find out why Naomi's family went to Moab.

SEECABU    FO    MENIFA

**2** ☐ **Pray.** ☐ **Read Ruth 1:8-14.** ☐ **Think about what you read using the three keys on the inside front cover.**
Circle the correct words to show what happened when Naomi left Moab.

Naomi told **Kilion/Ruth** and **Mahlon/Orpah** to **come/go/stay** home.

**Orpah/Ruth** kissed Naomi **good-bye/hello,** but **Orpah/Ruth clung/looked** to her.

**3** ☐ **Pray.** ☐ **Read Ruth 1:15-22.** ☐ **Think about what you read using the three keys on the inside front cover.**
Follow the maze to find out what Ruth said to Naomi.

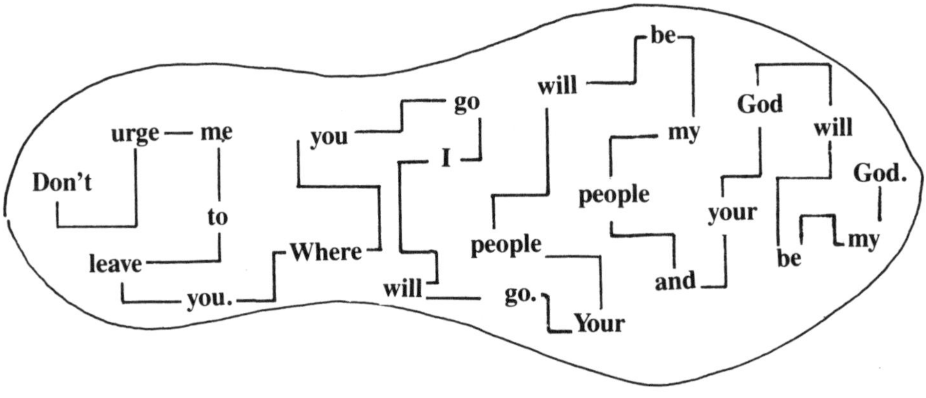

**4** ☐ **Pray.** ☐ **Read Ruth 2:1-7.** ☐ **Think about what you read using the three keys on the inside front cover.**
Use the code to see what happened when Ruth and Naomi reached Bethlehem.

| 0 = space | 1 = a | 2 = e | 3 = i | 4 = o | 5 = u |

R⬜th⬜p⬜ck⬜d⬜l⬜ft⬜v⬜r⬜gr⬜n

⬜⬜n⬜B⬜⬜z's⬜f⬜lds.

**5** ☐ **Pray.** ☐ **Read Ruth 2:8-16.** ☐ **Think about what you read using the three keys on the inside front cover.**

Use the code to find out what Boaz said to Ruth when she worked in his fields.

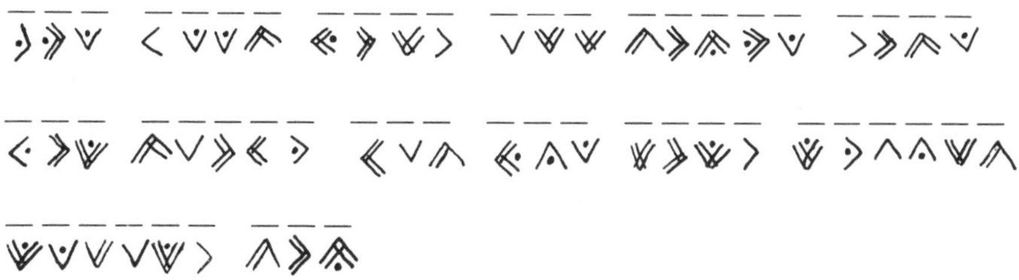

_(code key: A B C D; E F H I; L M N O; R T U V; W Y)_

_(coded message symbols)_

▶ ☐ **Weekend Review**

Recite your memory verse to an adult. This week, help plan, shop for, and cook a meal for your family. Write the menu in your notebook.

## WEEK 22 ☐ Memorize: Ruth 4:14

**1** ☐ **Pray.** ☐ **Read Ruth 2:17-23.** ☐ **Think about what you read using the three keys on the inside front cover.**

Separate the letters into words to find out what Naomi told Ruth about Boaz.

HEISOURCLOSERELATIVE

**2** ☐ **Pray.** ☐ **Read Ruth 3:1-6.** ☐ **Think about what you read using the three keys on the inside front cover.**

Fill in the puzzle with what Naomi told Ruth.

_(crossword grid with numbered squares 1–9)_

"I want to find a ____(8 Across) for you. Tonight Boaz will winnow ____(9 Across) on the ____(6 Across). ____(2 Down) and ____(4 Down) yourself, and put on your ____(1 Down) clothes. Go there, but don't let Boaz know you're there until he's done ____ (5 Across). When Boaz lies down, ____(3 Down) his ____(7 Down)."

**3** □ **Pray.** □ **Read Ruth 3:7-18.** □ **Think about what you read using the three keys on the inside front cover.**
Use the sounds of the objects to see what Boaz told Ruth at the threshing floor.

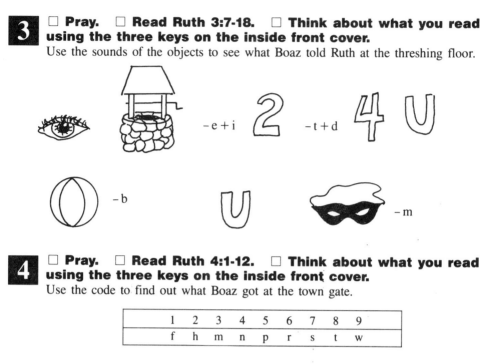

**4** □ **Pray.** □ **Read Ruth 4:1-12.** □ **Think about what you read using the three keys on the inside front cover.**
Use the code to find out what Boaz got at the town gate.

| | 1 | 2 | 3 | 4 | 5 | 6 | 7 | 8 | 9 |
|---|---|---|---|---|---|---|---|---|---|
| | f | h | m | n | p | r | s | t | w |

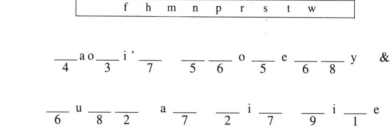

$$\underline{\quad} a o \underline{\quad} i \,' \underline{\quad} \quad \underline{\quad} \underline{\quad} o \underline{\quad} e \underline{\quad} \underline{\quad} y \quad \&$$
$$\underset{4}{\quad} \quad \underset{3}{\quad} \quad \underset{7}{\quad} \quad \underset{5}{\quad} \underset{6}{\quad} \quad \underset{5}{\quad} \quad \underset{6}{\quad} \underset{8}{\quad}$$

$$\underline{\quad} u \underline{\quad} \underline{\quad} \quad a \underline{\quad} \quad \underline{\quad} i \underline{\quad} \quad \underline{\quad} i \underline{\quad} e$$
$$\underset{6}{\quad} \quad \underset{8}{\quad} \underset{2}{\quad} \quad \underset{7}{\quad} \quad \underset{2}{\quad} \quad \underset{7}{\quad} \quad \underset{9}{\quad} \quad \underset{1}{\quad}$$

**5** □ **Pray.** □ **Read Ruth 4:13-22.** □ **Think about what you read using the three keys on the inside front cover.**
Connect the dashes to make the name of Ruth and Boaz's famous great-grandson.

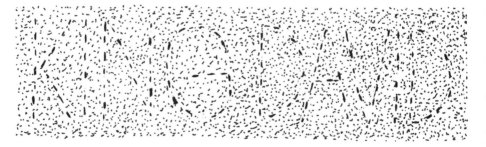

▶ □ **Weekend Review**
Recite your memory verse to an adult. This week, think of something nice you can do for a younger relative, such as sending a card or reading a story.

**1** ☐ **Pray.** ☐ **Read Matthew 25:1-13.** ☐ **Think about what you read using the three keys on the inside front cover.**

Find the words from Jesus' story about being ready for his return. They are hidden across, down, and diagonally.

| | | | | | | | | | | | | | | | |
|---|---|---|---|---|---|---|---|---|---|---|---|---|---|---|---|
| kingdom | five | W | F | O | O | L | I | S | H | M | O | D | G | N | I | K |
| heaven | foolish | T | I | J | Q | A | L | V | S | R | I | L | H | Y | U | R |
| virgins | wise | B | V | S | P | M | O | O | R | G | E | D | I | R | B | D |
| lamps | oil | U | E | M | E | P | H | E | A | V | E | N | C | O | Z | G |
| bridegroom | jars | S | L | K | O | S | T | Z | J | S | N | I | G | R | I | V |

**2** ☐ **Pray.** ☐ **Read Matthew 25:14-18.** ☐ **Think about what you read using the three keys on the inside front cover.**

To see what the man going away in Jesus' story did, write the words in order.

_____

3)money 2)his 1)entrusted 5)servants 4)to 8)their 6)according 7)to 9)ability

**3** ☐ **Pray.** ☐ **Read Matthew 25:19-30.** ☐ **Think about what you read using the three keys on the inside front cover.**

Use the code to find out what the returning master in Jesus' story said to the servants who had used his money wisely.

| 1 | 2 | 3 | 4 | 5 | 6 | 7 | 8 | 9 | 10 | 11 | 12 | 13 | 14 | 15 | 16 | 17 | 18 |
|---|---|---|---|---|---|---|---|---|---|---|---|---|---|---|---|---|---|
| A | C | E | F | G | H | I | L | M | N | O | P | R | S | T | U | W | Y |

_____ done. You've been _____
17  3  8  8                   4  1  7  15  6  4  16  8

with a _____ things. I will put you in _____
      4  3  17                              2  6  1  13  5  3

of _____. Come _____ my
   9  1  10  18        14  6  1  13  3

_____.
6  1  12  12  7  10  3  14  14

**4** ☐ **Pray.** ☐ **Read Matthew 25:31-40.** ☐ **Think about what you read using the three keys on the inside front cover.**

Finish the sentences to see who the people were kind to when they helped others.

I was in ☐ ___ ___ ___ and you visited me.

I was a ___ ___ ___ ___ ___ ___ ☐ ___ and you invited me in.

I was ___ ___ ___ ___ ☐ ___ and you gave me a drink.

I was ___ ☐ ___ ___ ___ ___ and you gave me food.

I was ☐ ___ ___ ___ and you looked after me.

**5** ☐ **Pray.** ☐ **Read Matthew 25:41-46.** ☐ **Think about what you read using the three keys on the inside front cover.**

Write the first letters of the objects to see what people will go to when Jesus returns.

Wicked people:  eternal  ___ ___ ___ ___ ___ ___ ___ ___ ___ ___ ___

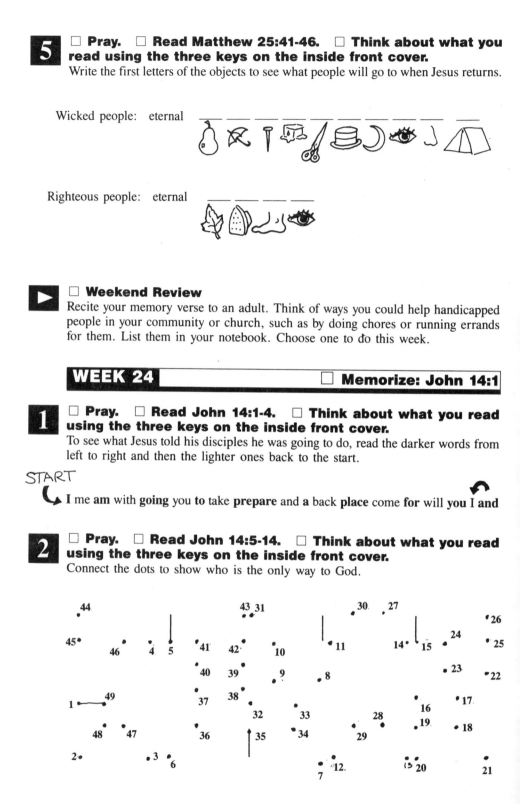

Righteous people:  eternal  ___ ___ ___ ___ ___

▶ ☐ **Weekend Review**

Recite your memory verse to an adult. Think of ways you could help handicapped people in your community or church, such as by doing chores or running errands for them. List them in your notebook. Choose one to do this week.

## WEEK 24                    ☐ Memorize: John 14:1

**1** ☐ **Pray.** ☐ **Read John 14:1-4.** ☐ **Think about what you read using the three keys on the inside front cover.**

To see what Jesus told his disciples he was going to do, read the darker words from left to right and then the lighter ones back to the start.

START

↳ I me **am** with **going** you **to** take **prepare** and **a** back **place** come **for** will **you I and**

**2** ☐ **Pray.** ☐ **Read John 14:5-14.** ☐ **Think about what you read using the three keys on the inside front cover.**

Connect the dots to show who is the only way to God.

**☐ Pray.   ☐ Read John 14:15-21.   ☐ Think about what you read using the three keys on the inside front cover.**

Use the code to find out what Jesus said to his disciples.

| me | if | what | you | command | obey | I | love |
|----|----|------|-----|---------|------|---|------|
| ▭ | ▯ | □ | ⊍ | ℂ | ◎ | ◇ | ♡ |

**☐ Pray.   ☐ Read John 14:22-27.   ☐ Think about what you read using the three keys on the inside front cover.**

Use the code to see what Jesus told the disciples about the Holy Spirit.

| 1 | 2 | 3 | 4 | 5 | 6 | 7 | 8 | 9 | 10 | 11 | 12 | 13 | 14 | 15 | 16 | 17 | 18 | 19 | 20 | 21 | 22 | 23 | 24 | 25 | 26 |
|---|---|---|---|---|---|---|---|---|----|----|----|----|----|----|----|----|----|----|----|----|----|----|----|----|----|
| a | b | c | d | e | f | g | h | i | j | k | l | m | n | o | p | q | r | s | t | u | v | w | x | y | z |

__ __   __ __ __ __   __ __ __ __ __   __ __ __
8  5    23 9 12 12    20 5 1 3 8       25 15 21

__ __ __   __ __ __ __ __ __   __ __ __
1  12 12   20 8 9 14 7 19      1 14 4

__ __ __ __ __ __   __ __ __   __ __   __ __ __
18 5 13 9 14 4      25 15 21   15 6    1 12 12

__   __ __ __ __
9    19 1 9 4

**☐ Pray.   ☐ Read John 14:28-31.   ☐ Think about what you read using the three keys on the inside front cover.**

Cross out the words Jesus did not say to his disciples about his death.

I'm going **away/home** and coming back to **earth/you.** If you loved me, you'd be **sad/glad** I'm going to the **Father/priests.** I've told you so you'll **run/believe.** Satan has no **sin/hold** on me. The world must learn I love the **disciples/Father** and do exactly what **he/they** commands.

**▶  ☐ Weekend Review**

Recite your memory verse to an adult. Plan and lead a family prayer or devotional time this week, perhaps at a meal or before bed. Write your plan in your notebook.

**1** ☐ **Pray.** ☐ **Read Matthew 27:11-26.** ☐ **Think about what you read using the three keys on the inside front cover.**
Write Pilate's questions and the crowd's answers in the correct speech balloons.

"What shall I do with Jesus?"
"Barabbas"

"Which one do you want set free?"
"Crucify him!"

**2** ☐ **Pray.** ☐ **Read Matthew 27:32-44.** ☐ **Think about what you read using the three keys on the inside front cover.**
Separate the letters into words to see what was on the sign on Jesus' cross.

## THISISJESUSTHEKINGOFTHEJEWS

**3** ☐ **Pray.** ☐ **Read Matthew 27:45-56.** ☐ **Think about what you read using the three keys on the inside front cover.**
Number the statements about Jesus' death in the correct order from 1 to 6.

_____ The centurion said, "Surely he was the Son of God!"

_____ Jesus cried in a loud voice and gave up his spirit.

_____ The earth shook and rocks split.

_____ Tombs broke open and people came back to life.

_____ The curtain of the temple was torn in two.

_____ Jesus cried, "My God, my God, why have you forsaken me?"

**4** ☐ **Pray.** ☐ **Read Matthew 28:1-10.** ☐ **Think about what you read using the three keys on the inside front cover.**
Use the code to find out what the angel told Mary Magdalene at the tomb.

| ⌒ | ⌒ | ⌒ | ☼ | ○ |
|---|---|---|---|---|
| A | E | I | O | space |

DO NOT BE AFRAID, FOR HE IS NOT

HERE. HE HAS RISEN.

**5** ☐ **Pray.** ☐ **Read Matthew 28:11-20.** ☐ **Think about what you read using the three keys on the inside front cover.**

Use the flag code to see what the risen Jesus told his disciples to do.

| All | Disciples | Go | Make | Nations | Of | And |
|-----|-----------|-----|------|---------|-----|-----|

☐ **Weekend Review**

Recite your memory verse to an adult. Ask your pastor for the name and address of a child your age from a missionary family. Write him or her this week.

## WEEK 26 ☐ Memorize: Acts 1:11b

**1** ☐ **Pray.** ☐ **Read Acts 1:1-11.** ☐ **Think about what you read using the three keys on the inside front cover.**

Read the message from right to left to find out what the disciples were told after Jesus was lifted up into heaven.

heaven into go him seen have you way same the in back come will Jesus same This

**2** ☐ **Pray.** ☐ **Read Acts 2:1-13.** ☐ **Think about what you read using the three keys on the inside front cover.**

Use the Morse code to find out what happened to the believers on Pentecost.

| •— | —•• | • | ••—• | •••• | •• | •—•• | ——— | •——• | •—• | ••• | — | •—— | —•—— |
|----|-----|---|------|------|-----|------|-----|------|-----|-----|---|-----|------|
| A | D | E | F | H | I | L | O | P | R | S | T | W | Y |

•— —•— •• •—•• •—••   •—— • •—• •   ••—• •• •—•• •—•• • —••

•—— •• — •••• — •••• •   •••• ——— •—•• —•—

••• •—• —•— •• •—• •• ——

**3** ☐ **Pray.** ☐ **Read Acts 2:14-21.** ☐ **Think about what you read using the three keys on the inside front cover.**

Match the phrases of the prophecy about the last days Peter said was coming true.

| | | |
|---|---|---|
| Your sons and daughters | On both men and women | will be saved. |
| God will pour out his Spirit. | Everyone who calls on the Lord | will prophesy. |

**4** ☐ **Pray.** ☐ **Read Acts 2:36-41.** ☐ **Think about what you read using the three keys on the inside front cover.**

Use the code to find out what Peter told the people he preached to.

| ✚ | ✟ | † | ✛ | † | + |
|---|---|---|---|---|---|
| a | e | i | o | u | space |

R✟p✟nt+✚nd+b✟+b✚pt†z✟d,+✟v✟ry+✛n✟++✛f+y✚†,+

_____

†n+th✟+n✚m✟++✛f+J✟s†s+Chr†st

**5** ☐ **Pray.** ☐ **Read Acts 2:42-47.** ☐ **Think about what you read using the three keys on the inside front cover.**

Check either the *yes* or *no* box for the things that the believers did.

Yes  No

☐    ☐   Ignored the apostles' teaching

☐    ☐   Shared some things

☐    ☐   Sold their things and gave to the needy

☐    ☐   Ate together at the temple

☐    ☐   Prayed and praised God together

▶ ☐ **Weekend Review**

Recite your memory verse to an adult. Think of something you can share with others in your church, such as your toys with nursery children or food for the hungry. Do it this week.

**1** ☐ **Pray.** ☐ **Read 1 Samuel 17:1-11.** ☐ **Think about what you read using the three keys on the inside front cover.**
Circle every other word to see what happened when Goliath gave his challenge.

Saul plus and David the Philistines Israelites became were so very happy afraid

**2** ☐ **Pray.** ☐ **Read 1 Samuel 17:12-24.** ☐ **Think about what you read using the three keys on the inside front cover.**
Put the correct numbers in the statements about David's going to his brothers.

# 1  3  8  10  10  40

For ___ days Goliath challenged the army of Israel. Jesse had ___ sons. The ___ oldest followed Saul to war. Jesse sent David to his brothers with ___ ephah of grain and ___ loaves of bread. He also sent ___ cheeses to their commander.

**3** ☐ **Pray.** ☐ **Read 1 Samuel 17:25-37.** ☐ **Think about what you read using the three keys on the inside front cover.**
Fill in the speech balloons with what David, his brother Eliab, and Saul said.

"I've killed a lion and a bear. God will save me from Goliath, too."
"Why have you come here? Who's taking care of the sheep?"
"I'll fight Goliath."
"Go, and the Lord be with you."
"Now what have I done? Can't I even speak?"
"You can't. You're only a boy."

| Eliab | David | David | Saul | David | Saul |

**4** ☐ **Pray.** ☐ **Read 1 Samuel 17:38-47.** ☐ **Think about what you read using the three keys on the inside front cover.**
Draw a line from each person to what he used for fighting.

javelin
staff
name of the Lord
armor
sword
5 smooth stones
spear
sling

David          Goliath

**5** ☐ **Pray.** ☐ **Read 1 Samuel 17:48-58.** ☐ **Think about what you read using the three keys on the inside front cover.**

Use the code to find out what happened when David and Goliath fought.

| 1 | 2 | 3 | 4 | 5 | 6 | 7 | 8 | 9 | 10 | 11 | 12 |
|---|---|---|---|---|---|---|---|---|----|----|----|
| D | G | H | L | M | N | P | R | S | T | V | W |

__ a __ i __   __ __iu__ __ __ e __   o __ e __
1   11  1   10 8  5 7 3  1   11  8

__ o __ i a __ __   __ i __ __   a   __ __ i __ __
2  4  10 3  12  10 3   9 4  6 2

a __ __   a __ __ o __ e
6 1   9 10  6

▶ ☐ **Weekend Review**

Recite your memory verse to an adult. In your notebook, draw a picture or write the story of how God has helped you in a hard situation. Tell a friend who is facing a hard situation about how God helped you and David.

---

**WEEK 28**      ☐ **Memorize: 1 Kings 4:29a**

**1** ☐ **Pray.** ☐ **Read 1 Kings 3:3-9.** ☐ **Think about what you read using the three keys on the inside front cover.**

Use the code to find out what Solomon asked God to give him.

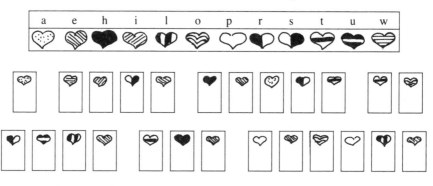

**2** ☐ **Pray.** ☐ **Read 1 Kings 3:10-15.** ☐ **Think about what you read using the three keys on the inside front cover.**

Circle the things God said he would give Solomon.

many children    a wise heart    riches    great armies    honor    a long life

**3** ☐ **Pray.** ☐ **Read 1 Kings 3:16-22.** ☐ **Think about what you read using the three keys on the inside front cover.**

Cross out all the question marks to see what Solomon was asked to decide.

?w?hi?cho??f?t??he?t?wow?o??men?w?ast??he?mot??he?r??o??f?t?he?li?vin??g?b?ab?y?

**4** ☐ **Pray.** ☐ **Read 1 Kings 3:23-28.** ☐ **Think about what you read using the three keys on the inside front cover.**

Number the conversations in the correct order to show what Solomon decided.

☐ "The living baby is mine!"—woman #1 & #2

☐ "Give her the living baby."—woman #1

☐ "Cut the living baby in two and give each woman half."—Solomon

☐ "Neither of us will have him."—woman #2

☐ "Give the living baby to the first woman. She's his mother." —Solomon

**5** ☐ **Pray.** ☐ **Read 1 Kings 4:29-34.** ☐ **Think about what you read using the three keys on the inside front cover.**

Find the things Solomon wrote or taught about wisely.

| proverbs | songs | A | N | I | M | A | L | S | O | M | T | E | L | S |
| plant life | birds | F | A | R | G | U | D | A | Z | O | Y | K | E | G |
| animals | fish | I | M | Y | P | R | O | V | E | R | B | S | O | N |
| reptiles | | S | E | L | I | T | P | E | R | E | S | T | V | O |
| | | H | O | B | E | F | I | L | T | N | A | L | P | S |

▶ ☐ **Weekend Review**

Recite your memory verse to an adult. In your notebook, keep track of decisions you have to make this week. List all the ways you could decide. Ask God to give you wisdom to choose the best. Write down your decisions and what happens later.

**1** ☐ **Pray.** ☐ **Read 1 Kings 18:1-2, 16-20.** ☐ **Think about what you read using the three keys on the inside front cover.**

Use the code to find out what the prophet Elijah told king Ahab to do.

| 1 | 2 | 3 | 4 | 5 |
|---|---|---|---|---|
| a | e | i | o | u |

T __ ll  t h __     p __ __ p l __     __ nd  t h __
  2      2       2  4     2     1        2

p r __ p h __ t s     __ f     B __ __ l     t __     m __ __ t
   4     2       4        1  1      4     2  2

m __ __ n     M __ __ n t     C __ rm __ l .
  2  4      4  5       1     2

**2** ☐ **Pray.** ☐ **Read 1 Kings 18:21-29.** ☐ **Think about what you read using the three keys on the inside front cover.**

Follow the words through the maze to find out what Elijah told the people.

```
     L B T M U W A A B E T Q T H E C O W H X P L L O W Y D
Start→H O W E O Q V E R X W B F B L Z L E I M Z O N Q H I M←Finish
     C Y L K Y L G D H E E J I K O P L K Q B K F D O M C W
     B P O Z D L B W T N Z N S N R B O V T U J X B G V J B
     W K N G W I T O B Z I O Q I D X F B I W M L I S G T K
     R T A J O R F O P I N B L S G O D A F B A A K N X Y P
```

**3** ☐ **Pray.** ☐ **Read 1 Kings 18:30-35.** ☐ **Think about what you read using the three keys on the inside front cover.**

Circle the correct word to show what Elijah did at the altar of the Lord.

Elijah repaired the altar with **24/12** stones and **dug/fixed** a trench around it. He poured **3/4 small/large** jars of **water/oil** on the **stones/wood** and **offering/priests.** He did this **2/3** times until the **trench/jars** overflowed.

**4** ☐ **Pray.** ☐ **Read 1 Kings 18:36-40.** ☐ **Think about what you read using the three keys on the inside front cover.**

Draw what happened after Elijah prayed to God and what the people said and did.

**5** ☐ **Pray.** ☐ **Read 1 Kings 18:41-45.** ☐ **Think about what you read using the three keys on the inside front cover.**
Find the words in the hidden picture to see what God sent.

——— —— —— — — —— ———

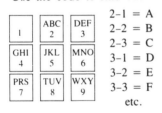 ☐ **Weekend Review**
Recite your memory verse to an adult. This week, interview an older Christian about reasons to follow God. List them in your notebook. Add your reasons, too.

---

## WEEK 30 ☐ Memorize: 2 Kings 5:15b

**1** ☐ **Pray.** ☐ **Read 2 Kings 5:1-6.** ☐ **Think about what you read using the three keys on the inside front cover.**
Use the code to find out what the young girl from Israel told Naaman's wife.

| 1 | ABC 2 | DEF 3 |
|---|---|---|
| GHI 4 | JKL 5 | MNO 6 |
| PRS 7 | TUV 8 | WXY 9 |

2-1 = A
2-2 = B
2-3 = C
3-1 = D
3-2 = E
3-3 = F
etc.

‾8-1‾ ‾4-2‾ ‾3-2‾  ‾7-1‾ ‾7-2‾ ‾6-3‾ ‾7-1‾ ‾4-2‾ ‾3-2‾ ‾8-1‾  ‾4-3‾ ‾6-2‾  ‾6-1‾ ‾9-3‾

‾2-3‾ ‾6-3‾ ‾8-2‾ ‾6-2‾ ‾8-1‾ ‾7-2‾ ‾9-3‾  ‾9-1‾ ‾6-3‾ ‾8-2‾ ‾5-3‾ ‾3-1‾

‾2-3‾ ‾8-2‾ ‾7-2‾ ‾3-2‾  ‾4-2‾ ‾4-3‾ ‾6-1‾

**2** ☐ **Pray.** ☐ **Read 2 Kings 5:7-10.** ☐ **Think about what you read using the three keys on the inside front cover.**
Cross out all the numbers except 7 to see what Elisha told Naaman to do.

4lW8a3s2h 7 4ti3m55els 9i3n3 t2h62e 9J4o32r8daln9 4R85i3vle23r9.

**3** ☐ **Pray.** ☐ **Read 2 Kings 5:11-14.** ☐ **Think about what you read using the three keys on the inside front cover.**

Do the crossword puzzle to see how Naaman felt when Elisha told him what to do.

Naaman was ____ (*3 Across*). He said, "I thought Elisha would ____ (*5 Across*) out to me, call on ____ (*4 Down*), wave his ____ (*8 Across*) over the spot, and ____ (*1 Down*) me. Aren't my nation's rivers better than any ____ (*2 Down*) of ____ (*7 Across*)? Couldn't I ____ (*6 Down*) in them?"

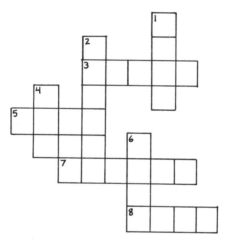

**4** ☐ **Pray.** ☐ **Read 2 Kings 5:15-19.** ☐ **Think about what you read using the three keys on the inside front cover.**

Skip all the words beginning with *M* to see what the healed Naaman told Elisha.

Maybe Now I must know make there is miracle no more man God in all the many music world money except must mark in May Israel mother.

**5** ☐ **Pray.** ☐ **Read 2 Kings 5:20-27.** ☐ **Think about what you read using the three keys on the inside front cover.**

Write the first letters of the animals to see what Elisha's servant got when he took gifts from Naaman and lied to Elisha.

____ ____ ____ ____ ____ ____

▶ ☐ **Weekend Review**

Recite your memory verse to an adult. This week, do something for someone who is sick. Some suggestions are to make a card, plant a flower in a pot, or bake a treat. Tell the sick person you are praying for him or her.

**1** ☐ **Pray.** ☐ **Read 2 Kings 22:1-7.** ☐ **Think about what you read using the three keys on the inside front cover.**

Use the pictures of objects and their sounds to find out what Josiah planned.

2  r+ 🐝 -b +  🍐  the  🕌  of the L +  🗡 -sw

**2** ☐ **Pray.** ☐ **Read 2 Kings 22:8-13.** ☐ **Think about what you read using the three keys on the inside front cover.**

Divide the words correctly to see why Josiah was upset after hearing God's Law.

Hek newt he Lordwa sang rybeca use thepeo plehad no tobe yedt heBo okoft heLaw.

**3** ☐ **Pray.** ☐ **Read 2 Kings 22:14-20.** ☐ **Think about what you read using the three keys on the inside front cover.**

Use the code to find out what the prophetess Huldah told Josiah that God said.

| A | B | D | | N | O | P |
|---|---|---|---|---|---|---|
| E | G | H | | R | S | T |
| I | L | M | | U | V | W |

Because your _____ was _____

and you _____ yourself before the _____, you will

not _____ all the _____ the Lord will

_____ on _____.

**4** ☐ **Pray.** ☐ **Read 2 Kings 23:1-7.** ☐ **Think about what you read using the three keys on the inside front cover.**

Mark the statements about Josiah and the people either *true* or *false*.

_____ Josiah and a few of the people went to the temple of the Lord.

_____ Josiah read all the words of the Book of the Covenant to the people.

_____ The Book of the Covenant had been found in the king's palace.

_____ Josiah renewed the covenant to follow the Lord with all his heart and soul.

_____ All the people promised to keep the covenant.

_____ Josiah kept all the places of worship and priests of other gods.

**5** ☐ **Pray.** ☐ **Read 2 Kings 23:22-25.** ☐ **Think about what you read using the three keys on the inside front cover.**
Follow the arrows to find out what kind of king Josiah was.

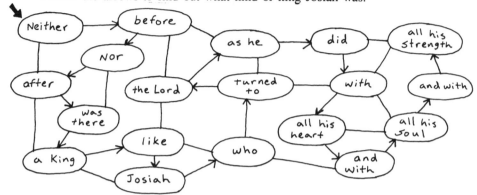

☐ **Weekend Review**
Recite your memory verse to an adult. Choose a passage of God's Word for your family to read together this week at dinner or before bed.

---

## WEEK 32             ☐ Memorize: Acts 5:12a

**1** ☐ **Pray.** ☐ **Read Acts 5:1-11.** ☐ **Think about what you read using the three keys on the inside front cover.**
Read the coins from small to large to see what Peter told Ananias about his gift.

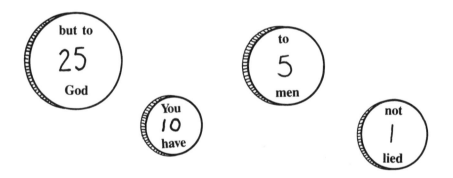

**2** ☐ **Pray.** ☐ **Read Acts 5:12-16.** ☐ **Think about what you read using the three keys on the inside front cover.**
Circle the correct words to show what the apostles did.

They did many **miracles/jobs** among the **rulers/people**. They were highly **feared/regarded** by the **priests/people**. People brought the **sick/rich** to the **streets/temple** to be **seen/healed** by them.

**3** ☐ **Pray.** ☐ **Read Acts 5:17-24.** ☐ **Think about what you read using the three keys on the inside front cover.**

Use the code to find out what happened after the apostles were put in jail.

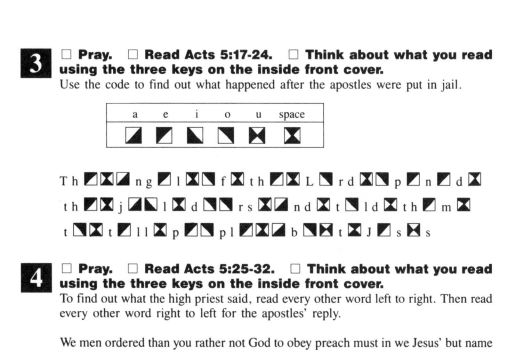

| a | e | i | o | u | space |
|---|---|---|---|---|---|

Th◻◻◻ng◻l◻◻f◻th◻◻◻L◻rd◻◻p◻n◻d◻
th◻◻j◻◻l◻d◻◻rs◻◻nd◻t◻ld◻th◻m◻
t◻◻t◻ll◻p◻◻pl◻◻◻b◻◻t◻J◻s◻s

**4** ☐ **Pray.** ☐ **Read Acts 5:25-32.** ☐ **Think about what you read using the three keys on the inside front cover.**

To find out what the high priest said, read every other word left to right. Then read every other word right to left for the apostles' reply.

We men ordered than you rather not God to obey preach must in we Jesus' but name

**5** ☐ **Pray.** ☐ **Read Acts 5:33-42.** ☐ **Think about what you read using the three keys on the inside front cover.**

Use the code to find out what the apostles did after being beaten and warned.

| 1 | 2 | 3 | 4 | 5 | 6 | 7 | 8 | 9 | 10 | 11 | 12 | 13 | 14 | 15 | 16 | 17 | 18 | 19 | 20 | 21 | 22 | 23 | 24 | 25 | 26 |
|---|---|---|---|---|---|---|---|---|----|----|----|----|----|----|----|----|----|----|----|----|----|----|----|----|----|
| z | y | x | w | v | u | t | s | r | q | p | o | n | m | l | k | j | i | h | g | f | e | d | c | b | a |

7 19 22 2    24 12 13 7 18 13 6 12 6 8 15 2

11 9 22 26 24 19 22 23    18 13    7 19 22

7 22 14 11 15 22    26 13 23    18 13

11 22 12 11 15 22 8    19 12 14 22 8    7 19 22

20 12 12 23    13 22 4 8    7 19 26 7

17 22 8 6 8    18 8    7 19 22    24 19 9 18 8 7

▶ ☐ **Weekend Review**

Recite your memory verse to an adult. In your notebook, list ways to help people who are being persecuted for their faith in Jesus. Some examples are helping to send them Bibles or collecting Christian magazines and books to send. Check with your pastor, and choose one to do this week.

**1** ☐ **Pray.** ☐ **Read Acts 8:1-8.** ☐ **Think about what you read using the three keys on the inside front cover.**
Unscramble the words to see what happened after persecution of the church began.

All except the **toeslaps** _____ were **treedcats** _____

throughout **daJue** _____ and Samaria, while **ulaS** _____ put

believers in **ripsno** _____.

**2** ☐ **Pray.** ☐ **Read Acts 8:26-35.** ☐ **Think about what you read using the three keys on the inside front cover.**
Draw a line from the quotes to who said them.

"Go to the chariot and                angel            "Go to the desert road."
stay near it."
                              Holy Spirit       "Do you understand what
"Jesus."                                          you're reading?"
                                Philip
"How can I unless someone                         "Who is the prophet
explains it?"               Ethiopian              talking about?"

**3** ☐ **Pray.** ☐ **Read Acts 8:36-40.** ☐ **Think about what you read using the three keys on the inside front cover.**
Finish the scene of what happened after the Ethiopian believed in Jesus.

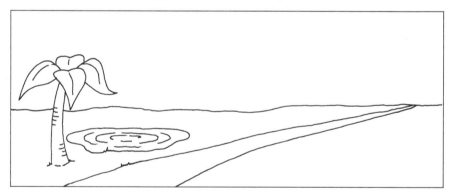

**4** ☐ **Pray.** ☐ **Read Acts 9:1-9.** ☐ **Think about what you read using the three keys on the inside front cover.**
Trace the Xs to form the letters of the name of the person Saul was persecuting.

```
V V U U U Y Y X X X X X X Z Z Z Y Y X X X X X H H H H X X X X X V V H X H H H H X H H H H X X X X Y Y Y Y Z Z Z Z
V V V V H H H H H X H H Y Y Y Z Z X Z Z V V V U U U X U U U H H H H X H H H H X H V V X V X V V V Z Z Z Z Y Y Y U
Z Y Y Y V V V V V X V U U U H H H X X X X X Y Y Y X X X X X V V V X V V V Z X Z Z Z Z X X X X Z Z Y Y U U U Z
H H H H U U U U U X U Z Z Z Y Y Y X Y Y H H H H H Y Y Y Y Z X Z Z Z Z X Z Z Z Z Z X Z H H H H H H X H H Y Y Y Y Y
Y Y V V V X V V V X V V H H U U U X U U Z Z Z Z Z H Z H H H X H H V X V V V V X V V V Y Y Y Y X U U U U U V V Y
H H Z Z Z X X X X X Z Y Y Y Y V X X X X X V V Y Y X X X X X Y Y Y X X X X X X Z Z Z Z X X X X Z Z Z Y Y Y Y H
```

**5** ☐ **Pray.** ☐ **Read Acts 9:10-19.** ☐ **Think about what you read using the three keys on the inside front cover.**

Use the code to find out what the Lord Jesus told Ananais about Saul.

| a ⬜ | e △ | i ◯ | o ☆ | u ◈ |
|---|---|---|---|---|

◯   h⬜v△   ch☆s△n   S⬜◈l   t☆

t△ll   n☆n-J△ws   ⬜b☆◈t   m△

▶ ☐ **Weekend Review**

Recite your memory verse to an adult. This week, read a Bible story or passage to a younger child, and help the child understand it.

## WEEK 34 ☐ Memorize: Acts 13:52

**1** ☐ **Pray.** ☐ **Read Acts 12:1-11.** ☐ **Think about what you read using the three keys on the inside front cover.**

Number the events in the correct order.

_____ King Herod put Peter in prison.

_____ The iron gate of the prison opened.

_____ The angel told Peter to put on his clothes and sandals.

_____ Peter realized God had rescued him.

_____ King Herod arrested some believers and killed James.

_____ Peter slept chained to two soldiers.

_____ The angel left Peter on the street.

_____ The church prayed earnestly to God for Peter.

_____ An angel woke Peter up.

_____ The angel led Peter out of prison.

_____ The chains fell off Peter's wrists.

**2** ☐ **Pray.** ☐ **Read Acts 12:12-19.** ☐ **Think about what you read using the three keys on the inside front cover.**

Fill in the blanks. The circled letters are the name of the person who told the message of Peter's escape to the believers.

Peter went to ___ ___ ◯ ___ 's house.

Many believers gathered ___ ◯ ___ ___ ___ to pray.

Peter ___ ___ ◯ ___ ___ ___ ___ at the outer entrance.

A servant girl answered the ◯ ___ ___ ___.

Leaving Peter outside, she ___ ◯ ___ back to tell the others.

**3** □ **Pray.** □ **Read Acts 13:1-12.** □ **Think about what you read using the three keys on the inside front cover.**

Use the braille code to find out what happened to the man who tried to keep others from faith in Jesus.

| A | B | D | E | I | L | M | N | T |
|---|---|---|---|---|---|---|---|---|

Paul _____ _____ _____ _____ him _____ _____ _____ _____ _____ for a _____ _____ _____ _____.

**4** □ **Pray.** □ **Read Acts 13:13-15, 38-43.** □ **Think about what you read using the three keys on the inside front cover.**

Cross out every other word to see the message Paul preached in the synagogue.

Through Moses Jesus gave there everything is made forgiveness for of pain sins.

**5** □ **Pray.** □ **Read Acts 13:44-52.** □ **Think about what you read using the three keys on the inside front cover.**

Follow the strings to the letters to see what the believers were filled with.

O   Y   Y   L   P   T

H   O   J   R   I   S   I

☐☐☐ & the ☐☐☐☐☐☐☐☐☐☐

▶ □ **Weekend Review**

Recite your memory verse to an adult. Get together with your family or a few friends to pray for people in your church or community.

**1** □ **Pray.** □ **Read Acts 18:1-11.** □ **Think about what you read using the three keys on the inside front cover.**

Match the names with the correct descriptions.

| | |
|---|---|
| Paul | emperor who ordered all Jews to leave Rome |
| Aquila and Priscilla | came from Macedonia to help Paul |
| Claudius | traveled from Athens to Corinth |
| Silas and Timothy | tentmakers who worked with Paul |
| Titius Justus | synagogue leader who believed in Jesus |
| Crispus | let Paul teach in his house |

**2** □ **Pray.** □ **Read Acts 18:18-23.** □ **Think about what you read using the three keys on the inside front cover.**

Follow the maze to see the people, places, and transportation of Paul's travels.

**3** □ **Pray.** □ **Read Acts 18:24-28.** □ **Think about what you read using the three keys on the inside front cover.**

Read the sentence from right to left to find out what happened to Apollos.

.better God of way the understand Apollos helped Aquila and Priscilla

**4** □ **Pray.** □ **Read Acts 19:1-12.** □ **Think about what you read using the three keys on the inside front cover.**

Use the code to see what God did in Ephesus.

| ⇉ | → | ➔ | → | ➡ | ▸ | → | ↔ | ➡ | ⇉ | ➡ | ➡ | ➡ | ⇉ | → | ⇚ | ← |
|---|---|---|---|---|---|---|---|---|---|---|---|---|---|---|---|---|
| A | C | D | E | G | H | I | L | M | O | P | R | S | T | U | V | Y |

**5** ☐ **Pray.** ☐ **Read Acts 19:13-22.** ☐ **Think about what you read using the three keys on the inside front cover.**
Put the words in their spots to find out what happened in Ephesus.

evil deeds / had practiced / name of Jesus

their expensive / new believers

The people held the _____ in great honor.
Many _____ confessed their _____
Some who _____ magic burned
_____ scrolls in public.

▶ ☐ **Weekend Review**
Recite your memory verse to an adult. On a world map, mark where missionaries from your church serve, and show it to your family or friends. Choose one missionary child about your age to send a postcard to.

## WEEK 36       ☐ Memorize: Acts 26:23

**1** ☐ **Pray.** ☐ **Read Acts 25:1-12.** ☐ **Think about what you read using the three keys on the inside front cover.**
Complete the crossword puzzle about Paul's trial before Festus.

The chief _____ (2 Across) went before Festus with serious _____ (1 Down) against _____ (2 Down). They wanted _____ (6 Across) to send Paul to _____ (5 Across) for trial. They planned an _____ (3 Down) to kill Paul along the way. Paul said, "I have not done _____ (4 Down) wrong. I _____ (3 Across) to Caesar for my trial!"

**2** ☐ **Pray.** ☐ **Read Acts 25:13-22.** ☐ **Think about what you read using the three keys on the inside front cover.**
Read only the capital letters to find out what Agrippa said to Festus about Paul.

f In We Owl Up Lo Do Law In Key Eat Ten Ox Hi Egg All Red Too Hen Ice Sad Me And No Met You So Eel Look Far

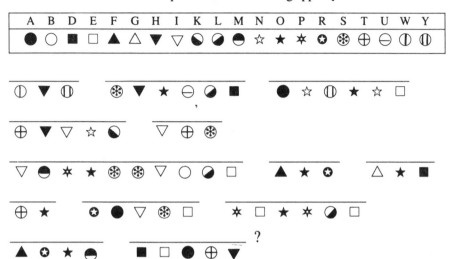

**3** ☐ **Pray.** ☐ **Read Acts 26:1-11.** ☐ **Think about what you read using the three keys on the inside front cover.**

Use the code to find out the question Paul asked Agrippa. .

| A | B | D | E | F | G | H | I | K | L | M | N | O | P | R | S | T | U | W | Y |
|---|---|---|---|---|---|---|---|---|---|---|---|---|---|---|---|---|---|---|---|
| ● | ○ | ■ | □ | ▲ | △ | ▼ | ▽ | ◖ | ◑ | ◕ | ☆ | ★ | ✳ | ✪ | ✸ | ⊕ | ⊖ | ◐ | ◑ |

_(coded puzzle message, ending with a "?")_

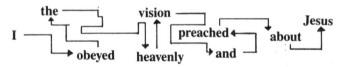

**4** ☐ **Pray.** ☐ **Read Acts 26:12-23.** ☐ **Think about what you read using the three keys on the inside front cover.**

Starting with *I*, follow the arrows to find out what Paul said about himself.

the — vision — Jesus
I — preached ← about
obeyed   heavenly   and

**5** ☐ **Pray.** ☐ **Read Acts 26:24-32.** ☐ **Think about what you read using the three keys on the inside front cover.**

Put the number of the quotes in the speech balloon of the person who said them.

Festus   Paul   Agrippa   Paul   listeners to Paul   Agrippa

1. "Do you think you can persuade me so fast?"
2. "He could go free, but he asked to have a trial by Caesar."
3. "No, what I say is true."
4. "There's no reason to punish him."
5. "I want everyone to be a Christian."
6. "You're out of your mind!"

▶ ☐ **Weekend Review**

Recite your memory verse to an adult. Imagine you have to explain in court what you believe about Jesus. Write it in your notebook, and read it to a friend or family member.

**1** ☐ **Pray.** ☐ **Read Psalm 1:1-3.** ☐ **Think about what you read using the three keys on the inside front cover.**
Complete the picture of what the person who follows God is like.

**2** ☐ **Pray.** ☐ **Read Psalm 1:4-6.** ☐ **Think about what you read using the three keys on the inside front cover.**
Follow the lines to see what happens to wicked and righteous people.

the way of the righteous

the way of the wicked

the Lord watches over

will perish

**3** ☐ **Pray.** ☐ **Read Psalm 15:1-5.** ☐ **Think about what you read using the three keys on the inside front cover.**
Circle the words that tell about the person who pleases God.

The one who is **blameless/crooked,** who **covers/speaks** the truth, who treats **neighbors/family** kindly, who keeps **promises/money,** who **lends/keeps** money.

**4** ☐ **Pray.** ☐ **Read Psalm 24:1-6.** ☐ **Think about what you read using the three keys on the inside front cover.**
Use the code to find out what the psalmist said about God.

| Z | A | B | C | D | E | F | G | H | I | J | K | L | M | N | O | P | Q | R | S | T | U | V | W | X | Y | ! |
|---|---|---|---|---|---|---|---|---|---|---|---|---|---|---|---|---|---|---|---|---|---|---|---|---|---|---|
| A | B | C | D | E | F | G | H | I | J | K | L | M | N | O | P | Q | R | S | T | U | V | W | X | Y | Z | space |

S g d ! d z q s g ! h r ! s g d ! K n q c r ! z m c ! d u d q x s g h m f ! h m !

h s , ! s g d ! v n q k c ! z m c ! z k k ! v g n ! k h u d ! h m ! h s .

**5** ☐ **Pray.** ☐ **Read Psalm 24:7-10.** ☐ **Think about what you read using the three keys on the inside front cover.**

Read the words made of large and small letters to see who the King of glory is.

T E | R | T R | N | G H | I | AT
H | O D | ON G | D | T Y | N T LE

☐ **Weekend Review**

Recite your memory verse to an adult. In your notebook, write your own psalm to God, and then share it with your family this week.

## WEEK 38 ☐ Memorize: Psalm 150:6

**1** ☐ **Pray.** ☐ **Read Psalm 148:1-6.** ☐ **Think about what you read using the three keys on the inside front cover.**

Use the code to see why the psalmist said everything should praise the Lord.

| 1 | 2 | 3 | 4 | 5 | 6 | 7 | 8 | 9 | 10 | * |
|---|---|---|---|---|---|---|---|---|---|---|
| c | d | f | h | m | n | r | t | w | y | space |

___ o ___ * ___ e * ___ o ___ ___ a ___ ___ e ___ * a___ *
 3     7     4     1    5  5    6  2    2    6 2

___ ___ e ___ * ___ e ___ e * ___ e a ___ e ___
 8  4    10    9   7    1 7    8    2

**2** ☐ **Pray.** ☐ **Read Psalm 148:7-12.** ☐ **Think about what you read using the three keys on the inside front cover.**

Finish the vertical words of the things the psalmist said should praise the Lord.

```
                                      L
                  B           M       ___
                  ___         O   G               W
              A R C           ___   H       H     I
          N ___ ___ ___       N     ___     ___   T ___
      P R A I S E             T H E         L O R D
      E ___ T M   A           ___ A N       L C ___ ___
      ___ L ___ ___   ___     ___ ___ ___   ___ ___ E
      P E ___ L   U           N ___ N       ___ ___
      L ___ N ___   R         ___   ___     N
      ___ ___ ___   ___
                    ___
```

**3** ☐ **Pray.** ☐ **Read Psalm 148:13-14.** ☐ **Think about what you read using the three keys on the inside front cover.**

Match the words to the pictures to find out what the psalmist said about God.

the heavens
the earth
is above
splendor

His ☀ ⬆ 🌍 & 🌙

**4** ☐ **Pray.** ☐ **Read Psalm 149:1-9.** ☐ **Think about what you read using the three keys on the inside front cover.**

Use the note code to find out what the psalmist said to do.

**5** ☐ **Pray.** ☐ **Read Psalm 150:1-6.** ☐ **Think about what you read using the three keys on the inside front cover.**

Unscramble the words to find out what the psalmist said about praise.

Let **greenthivy** _____ that has **ratbeh** _____

**aresip** _____ the **rodL** _____

▶ ☐ **Weekend Review**

Recite your memory verse to an adult. With a few friends, play a musical instrument or sing a song of praise for your church or family this week. You may want to write the song, too.

**1**  ☐ **Pray.**  ☐ **Read Proverbs 3:1-6.**  ☐ **Think about what you read using the three keys on the inside front cover.**

Follow the line through the words to read what Proverbs says to do.

all  with  Lord  on  (not)  ways  him  and  will  paths
the  in  your  and  your  your  all  in  acknowledge
trust  heart  lean  own  understanding  he  direct  your

**2**  ☐ **Pray.**  ☐ **Read Proverbs 3:7-12.**  ☐ **Think about what you read using the three keys on the inside front cover.**

Mark the messages in the signs from Proverbs either "Do" or "Don't."

Do        Don't

Think you are wise   Go away from evil   Fear God   Honor God with your money   Despise God's discipline   Resent God's rebuke

**3**  ☐ **Pray.**  ☐ **Read Proverbs 3:21-28.**  ☐ **Think about what you read using the three keys on the inside front cover.**

Cross out the Zs to find out what Proverbs says about being afraid.

ZZTZHEZLOZRZDWZILLZBZZEYZOUZRZZCOZNZFIZDEZZNZCZEZZZ
ZZAZZNZDKEZZEPZYOZZUZSAZFZEZZZ

**4**  ☐ **Pray.**  ☐ **Read Proverbs 17:1-6.**  ☐ **Think about what you read using the three keys on the inside front cover.**

Use the code to see what Proverbs says about families.

| ① | ❶ | ② | ❷ | ③ | ❸ | ④ | ❹ | ⑤ | ❺ | ⑥ | ❻ | ⑦ | ❼ | ⑧ | ❽ | © |
|---|---|---|---|---|---|---|---|---|---|---|---|---|---|---|---|---|
| A | C | D | E | F | G | H | I | L | N | O | P | R | S | T | W | space |

❸⑦①❺②❶④❹⑤②⑦❷❺©①⑦❷©①©❶⑦⑥❽❺©❽⑥©❽④❷©

⑥❺②©①❺②©❻①⑦❷❺❽❼©①⑦❷©❽④❷©⑥⑦❹②❷©❻③©

❽④❷❹⑦©❶④❹⑤②⑦❷❺

**5** ☐ **Pray.** ☐ **Read Proverbs 17:17-22.** ☐ **Think about what you read using the three keys on the inside front cover.**

To find two proverbs, read every other word left to right and then back again.

A MEDICINE FRIEND GOOD LOVES IS AT HEART ALL CHEERFUL TIMES A

▶ ☐ **Weekend Review**

Recite your memory verse to an adult. Choose a proverb for your family. Write it, frame it, and hang it up in your home.

A cheerful
heart is
good medicine

## WEEK 40                    ☐ Memorize: Isaiah 53:6

**1** ☐ **Pray.** ☐ **Read Isaiah 53:1-3.** ☐ **Think about what you read using the three keys on the inside front cover.**

To see the name of the person described by the prophet Isaiah, shade in the squares marked with only one line.

**2** ☐ **Pray.** ☐ **Read Isaiah 53:4-6.** ☐ **Think about what you read using the three keys on the inside front cover.**

To see what Isaiah said about people, read the arrows that point only right.

We⟩ ⟨They    all⟩ like⟩⟨not⟩ ⟨us    sheep⟩ have⟩ ⟨not⟩ gone⟩ ⟨wanted

⟨that⟩ astray⟩ and⟩ God⟩⟨said⟩ laid⟩ our⟩⟨wants⟩ sins⟩⟨over on⟩⟨us⟩ Jesus⟩

**3** ☐ **Pray.** ☐ **Read Isaiah 53:7-8.** ☐ **Think about what you read using the three keys on the inside front cover.**

Cross out every third letter to see what Isaiah said Jesus would do at his trial.

## HERDIPDNAOTHOPTENDHIMSMIOURTHE

**4** ☐ **Pray.** ☐ **Read Isaiah 53:9-10.** ☐ **Think about what you read using the three keys on the inside front cover.**

Do the math problems, and then use the code to find out what kind of people Isaiah said Jesus would die and be buried with.

| 1=A | 2=C | 3=D | 4=E | 5=H | 6=I | 7=K | 8=N | 9=R | 10=T | 11=W |
|---|---|---|---|---|---|---|---|---|---|---|

| 9 | 20 | 3 | 19 | | 25 | 3 | 11 |
|---|---|---|---|---|---|---|---|
| +2 | −14 | +7 | −14 | | −15 | +2 | −7 |

☐ ☐ ☐ ☐   ☐ ☐ ☐

\_\_ \_\_ \_\_ \_\_   \_\_ \_\_ \_\_

| 8 | 14 | 23 | 12 | 18 | 9 | | 29 | 5 | 15 |
|---|---|---|---|---|---|---|---|---|---|
| +3 | −8 | −21 | −5 | −14 | −6 | | −28 | +3 | −12 |

☐ ☐ ☐ ☐ ☐ ☐   ☐ ☐ ☐

\_\_ \_\_ \_\_ \_\_ \_\_ \_\_   \_\_ \_\_ \_\_

| 6 | 11 | 16 | | 20 | 13 | 17 | 4 |
|---|---|---|---|---|---|---|---|
| +4 | −6 | −12 | | −11 | −7 | −15 | +1 |

☐ ☐ ☐   ☐ ☐ ☐ ☐

\_\_ \_\_ \_\_   \_\_ \_\_ \_\_ \_\_

**5** ☐ **Pray.** ☐ **Read Isaiah 53:11-12.** ☐ **Think about what you read using the three keys on the inside front cover.**

Use the code to find out what Isaiah said would happen to Jesus.

| a | e | i | o | u |
|---|---|---|---|---|
| ☆ | ✪ | ✳ | ✫ | ✷ |

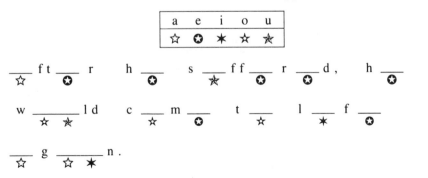

\_\_ f t \_\_ r   h \_\_   s \_\_ f f \_\_ r \_\_ d ,   h \_\_
☆    ✪       ✪      ✷    ✪   ✪          ✪

w \_\_\_\_ l d   c \_\_ m \_\_   t \_\_   l \_\_ f \_\_
   ✫  ✷       ☆    ✪      ☆      ✳   ✪

\_\_ g \_\_ \_\_ n .
☆    ☆ ✷

☐ **Weekend Review**

Recite your memory verse to an adult. Make your own coded message about what you learned about Jesus this week. Give it to a friend or family member to solve.

**1** ☐ **Pray.** ☐ **Read Romans 8:1-8.** ☐ **Think about what you read using the three keys on the inside front cover.**
Cross out the capital letters to find out what God did for us.

The seEnOt hEMisT DowInO sLoWnEW StoNE bEe SanD LoWflfeSPringO fRoMr sAiLOnE.

**2** ☐ **Pray.** ☐ **Read Romans 8:9-17.** ☐ **Think about what you read using the three keys on the inside front cover.**
Use the code to find out what the Spirit says believers in Jesus are.

| 0=space  1=A  2=E  3=I  4=O |
| --- |

Th ☐ y ☐ ☐ r ☐ ☐ G ☐ d's ☐ ch ☐ ldr ☐ n

**3** ☐ **Pray.** ☐ **Read Romans 8:18-27.** ☐ **Think about what you read using the three keys on the inside front cover.**
Connect the dashes to see who helps us to pray and prays to God for us.

**4** ☐ **Pray.** ☐ **Read Romans 8:28-30.** ☐ **Think about what you read using the three keys on the inside front cover.**
Use the code to find out what God does in all things that happen.

| + | * | – | < | > | # | % | • | / | = | ≠ | ÷ | × | ♭ | ⟨ | √ | ° |
| --- | --- | --- | --- | --- | --- | --- | --- | --- | --- | --- | --- | --- | --- | --- | --- | --- |
| D | E | F | G | H | I | K | L | M | N | O | R | S | T | V | W | space |

< ≠ + °√ ≠ ÷ % × ° – ≠ ÷ °♭ > * °< ≠ ≠ + ° ≠ – °

♭ > ≠ × * °√ > ≠ ° • ≠⟨ * ° > # /

**5** ☐ **Pray.** ☐ **Read Romans 8:31-39.** ☐ **Think about what you read using the three keys on the inside front cover.**

Circle what can separate Christians from God's love. Then cross out what cannot separate Christians from God's love.

danger, troubles angels problems hunger persecution powers

demons life death nothing the present the future height depth

▶ ☐ **Weekend Review**

Recite your memory verse to an adult. On a card, write a favorite verse from this week's Bible readings. Post it in your room, and practice reciting it.

## WEEK 42 ☐ Memorize: 1 Corinthians 13:13

**1** ☐ **Pray.** ☐ **Read 1 Corinthians 12:1-6.** ☐ **Think about what you read using the three keys on the inside front cover.**

Read every other word left to right. Then read every other word right to left to find out what the apostle Paul said about spiritual gifts.

The God different same kinds the of from gifts, are service, working and

**2** ☐ **Pray.** ☐ **Read 1 Corinthians 12:7-11.** ☐ **Think about what you read using the three keys on the inside front cover.**

Search for the words about the gifts of the Holy Spirit.

| speaking | E A T O E M O S P E A K I N G S |
| wisdom | M T O R E D I R E D B R N Z O O |
| knowledge | O R N Q B E G D E L W O N K W A |
| languages | H A H S A C K O P A C E D W I N |
| interpretation | Z U M R H E A L I N G A M E S S |
| faith | E L Q T Y S E H P O R P R I D E |
| healing | T W I N T E R P R E T A T I O N |
| miracles | A A N K M I N E X L A T U N M Y |
| prophesy | F A L L S E G A U G N A L R E D |

**3** ☐ **Pray.** ☐ **Read 1 Corinthians 12:12-20, 27-31.** ☐ **Think about what you read using the three keys on the inside front cover.**

Use the code to find out what believers in Jesus are.

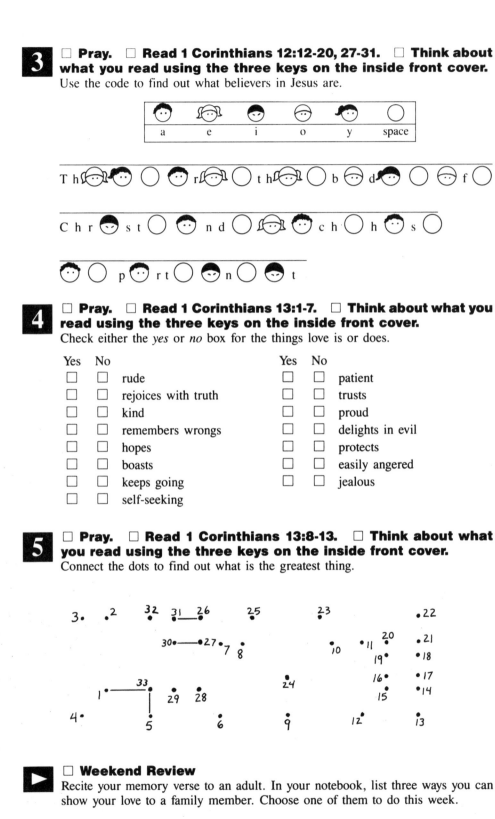

| a | e | i | o | y | space |

T h ___ ___ ___ ___ r ___ ___ t h ___ ___ b ___ d ___ ___ ___ f ___

C h r ___ s t ___ ___ n d ___ ___ ___ c h ___ h ___ s ___

___ ___ p ___ r t ___ ___ n ___ ___ t

**4** ☐ **Pray.** ☐ **Read 1 Corinthians 13:1-7.** ☐ **Think about what you read using the three keys on the inside front cover.**

Check either the *yes* or *no* box for the things love is or does.

| Yes | No | | Yes | No | |
|-----|-----|--------------------|-----|-----|----------------|
| ☐ | ☐ | rude | ☐ | ☐ | patient |
| ☐ | ☐ | rejoices with truth | ☐ | ☐ | trusts |
| ☐ | ☐ | kind | ☐ | ☐ | proud |
| ☐ | ☐ | remembers wrongs | ☐ | ☐ | delights in evil |
| ☐ | ☐ | hopes | ☐ | ☐ | protects |
| ☐ | ☐ | boasts | ☐ | ☐ | easily angered |
| ☐ | ☐ | keeps going | ☐ | ☐ | jealous |
| ☐ | ☐ | self-seeking | | | |

**5** ☐ **Pray.** ☐ **Read 1 Corinthians 13:8-13.** ☐ **Think about what you read using the three keys on the inside front cover.**

Connect the dots to find out what is the greatest thing.

▶ ☐ **Weekend Review**

Recite your memory verse to an adult. In your notebook, list three ways you can show your love to a family member. Choose one of them to do this week.

**1** □ **Pray.** □ **Read Galatians 5:1-6.** □ **Think about what you read using the three keys on the inside front cover.**

Cross out the *D*s to find out what the apostle Paul said is most important.

DThedtdhidndgdthadtcdodundtsdidsfdadidtthddexpdressdingdidtdsedlfdthdrodugdhldove.

**2** □ **Pray.** □ **Read Galatians 5:13-18.** □ **Think about what you read using the three keys on the inside front cover.**

Use the code to find out the command that sums up the whole law.

| 1 | 2 | 3 | 4 | 5 | 6 | 7 | 8 | 9 | 10 | 11 | 12 | 13 | 14 | 15 | 16 | 17 | 18 | 19 | 20 | 21 | 22 | 23 | 24 | 25 | 26 |
|---|---|---|---|---|---|---|---|---|----|----|----|----|----|----|----|----|----|----|----|----|----|----|----|----|----|
| a | b | c | d | e | f | g | h | i | j | k | l | m | n | o | p | q | r | s | t | u | v | w | x | y | z |

___ ___ ___ ___      ___ ___ ___ ___      ___ ___ ___ ___ ___ ___ ___ ___
12  15  22  5       25  15  21  18       14   5   9   7   8   2  15  18

___ ___      ___ ___ ___ ___ ___ ___ ___ ___
 1  19       25  15  21  18  19   5  12   6

**3** □ **Pray.** □ **Read Galatians 5:19-26.** □ **Think about what you read using the three keys on the inside front cover.**

Fill in the letters of the fruit of the Spirit.

```
                                            G
F                                           —
—                                           —
I         G      S          L      D        P
—         —      —          —      —        —
—    K    —  J   —          —      —        —
F R  U  I T  O F      T H E      S P I R I T
—         —  —   —          —     — —      — —
—      — E       —                A       N
—      N —       N                — —     — —
—      — — —     —                E       E
—      — — —     R
S      S S       —
                 L
```

**4** □ **Pray.** □ **Read Galatians 6:1-6.** □ **Think about what you read using the three keys on the inside front cover.**

Use the code to find out what the apostle Paul said believers should do.

| ◖ | ◒ | ◐ | ◑ | ◓ | ◗ |
|---|---|---|---|---|---|
| a | e | i | o | u | space |

H ___ l p ___ ___ ___ c h ___ ___ t h ___ r ___ w ___ t h ___

t r ___ ___ b l ___ s ___ ___ n d ___ f ___ l f ___ l l ___ t h ___

l ___ w ___ ___ f ___ C h r ___ s t ___ t h ___ s ___ w ___ y.

5

☐ **Pray.** ☐ **Read Galatians 6:7-10.** ☐ **Think about what you read using the three keys on the inside front cover.**

Write in the words from the correct puzzle piece to see what Paul said.

| | |
|---|---|
| 1)<br>As you<br>have | 2)<br>the opportunity |
| 3)<br>do good | |

4)<br>to all<br>people

4)<br>work for<br>good pay

4)<br>to<br>Christians<br>only

4)<br>sometimes

▶ ☐ **Weekend Review**

Recite your memory verse to an adult. In your notebook, list three ways you can be kind to a neighbor, such as by helping with yard work, running an errand, or babysitting. Choose one to do this week.

## WEEK 44 ☐ Memorize: Philippians 2:4

**1** ☐ **Pray.** ☐ **Read Philippians 2:1-4.** ☐ **Think about what you read using the three keys on the inside front cover.**

Separate the letters into words to find out what the apostle Paul said to do.

Eachofyoushouldlooknotonlytoyourowninterestsbutalsototheinterestsofothers.

**2** ☐ **Pray.** ☐ **Read Philippians 2:5-11.** ☐ **Think about what you read using the three keys on the inside front cover.**

Use the code to see who God wants to bow and confess that Jesus is Lord.

| A | D | E | H | I | N | O | R | T | U | V | Y |
|---|---|---|---|---|---|---|---|---|---|---|---|

**3** ☐ **Pray.** ☐ **Read Philippians 2:14-18.** ☐ **Think about what you read using the three keys on the inside front cover.**

To find out how to shine like stars for God, on the line below, write the letters from the stars with four points. Then separate them into words.

(Stars containing letters:)

I D n o t e v e t r y
t h e r i n g w i t s
h o w u s t a c o m e
p l a y v i n e s i n
g f o r c a r g l u e
t h i n g

_____

_____

**4** ☐ **Pray.** ☐ **Read Philippians 3:1-11.** ☐ **Think about what you read using the three keys on the inside front cover.**

Follow the words through the maze to see what Paul said is important.

Start

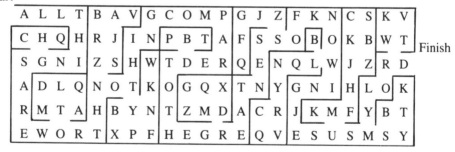

| A | L | L | T | B | A | V | G | C | O | M | P | G | J | Z | F | K | N | C | S | K | V |
| C | H | Q | H | R | J | I | N | P | B | T | A | F | S | S | O | B | O | K | B | W | T |
| S | G | N | I | Z | S | H | W | T | D | E | R | Q | E | N | Q | L | W | J | Z | R | D |
| A | D | L | Q | N | O | T | K | O | G | Q | X | T | N | Y | G | N | I | H | L | O | K |
| R | M | T | A | H | B | Y | N | T | Z | M | D | A | C | R | J | K | M | F | Y | B | T |
| E | W | O | R | T | X | P | F | H | E | G | R | E | Q | V | E | S | U | S | M | S | Y |

Finish

**5** ☐ **Pray.** ☐ **Read Philippians 3:12-16.** ☐ **Think about what you read using the three keys on the inside front cover.**

Cross out the wrong words to see what Paul's goal was.

**Forgetting/Remembering** the **things/people** that are **ahead/past** and **straining/crying** hard for what is **ahead/past**, I **press/walk** on toward the **path/goal** to **win/lose** the **race/prize** for which **man/God** has **called/refused** me.

▶ ☐ **Weekend Review**

Recite your memory verse to an adult. Choose a family member to help this week. In your notebook, list three ways to help, and then do one of them this week.

**1** ☐ **Pray.** ☐ **Read Ezekiel 34:1-6.** ☐ **Think about what you read using the three keys on the inside front cover.**

Hold your book up to a mirror to translate the backwards message and see why God said he would punish the leaders of his people, Israel.

THEYONLYTAKECAREOFTHEMSELVES

**2** ☐ **Pray.** ☐ **Read Ezekiel 34:7-10.** ☐ **Think about what you read using the three keys on the inside front cover.**

Use the code to find out what God said he would do about the bad leaders.

| ¶ | 9 | ◖ | ℂ | 6 | ◼ |
|---|---|---|---|---|---|
| A | E | I | O | U | space |

_____ w ___l l___ r ___m___ v _____ th___m _____nd___
◖ ◼ ◖ ◼ 9 ℂ 9 ◼ 9 ◼ ¶ ◼

r ___sc_____ m y ___ p _____pl _____ fr ___m___th___m
9 6 9 ◼ ◼ 9 ℂ 9 ◼ ℂ ◼ 9

**3** ☐ **Pray.** ☐ **Read Ezekiel 34:11-16.** ☐ **Think about what you read using the three keys on the inside front cover.**

Solve the crossword puzzle to see what God said he would do for his people.

I'll _____ (*4 Across*) for my sheep and look _____ (*8 Across*) them. I'll _____ (*2 Down*) them and bring them into their own _____ (*1 Down*). I myself will _____ (*6 Across*) my sheep. I'll search for the _____ (*1 Across*) and bring back the _____ (*5 Down*). I'll care for the _____ (*3 Down*) and strengthen the _____ (*9 Across*). I will _____ (*10 Across*) them with _____ (*7 Across*).

**4** ☐ **Pray.** ☐ **Read Ezekiel 34:17-24.** ☐ **Think about what you read using the three keys on the inside front cover.**

To find out what God said he would do to the people, first read the words in the sheep facing right, and then read the words in the sheep facing left.

I one will person judge and between another

**5** ☐ **Pray.** ☐ **Read Ezekiel 34:25-31.** ☐ **Think about what you read using the three keys on the inside front cover.**
Check either the *yes* or *no* box about the things God promised his people.

Yes    No

☐    ☐    God will make a covenant of peace with them.
☐    ☐    Wild beasts will overrun their land.
☐    ☐    They will live and sleep in safety.
☐    ☐    They will have good crops.
☐    ☐    God will not send showers in season.
☐    ☐    They will not be sure if God is with them.

▶ ☐ **Weekend Review**
Recite your memory verse to an adult. Make a coded message about what you learned about God in this week's Bible readings. Give it to a friend to solve.

## WEEK 46    ☐ Memorize: Daniel 3:17

**1** ☐ **Pray.** ☐ **Read Daniel 3:1-6.** ☐ **Think about what you read using the three keys on the inside front cover.**
Search for the words about what King Nebuchadnezzar did.

```
O  T  H  E  R  A  L  D  L  W  S  E  C  N  I  V  O  R  P  Q  S
N  B  A  R  S  U  N  A  E  E  K  I  N  G  Z  B  T  R  O  D  E
I  X  R  E  H  T  I  Z  G  T  S  E  N  A  T  I  O  N  S  H  E
A  C  P  E  O  P  L  E  A  U  F  U  R  N  A  C  E  N  T  E  N
L  I  S  O  U  N  D  D  M  L  Z  B  O  Y  G  N  I  Z  A  L  B
P  I  H  S  R  O  W  O  I  F  I  N  H  O  L  B  A  T  Z  M  I
```

image  plain  province  herald  people  nations  sound  horn  flute  zither
lyre  harp  pipes  music  worship  king  blazing  furnace

**2** ☐ **Pray.** ☐ **Read Daniel 3:7-12.** ☐ **Think about what you read using the three keys on the inside front cover.**
Write the letter of the alphabet that comes *before* each letter to find out what some people told the king about Shadrach, Meshach, and Abednego.

———————————————————————————————————

P  Ljoh,  uifz  epo'u  xpstijq  uif  jnbhf  pg

———————————————————————————————————

hpme  zpv  ibwf  tfu  vq.

**3** ☐ **Pray.** ☐ **Read Daniel 3:13-18.** ☐ **Think about what you read using the three keys on the inside front cover.**
Match the quotes to who said them.

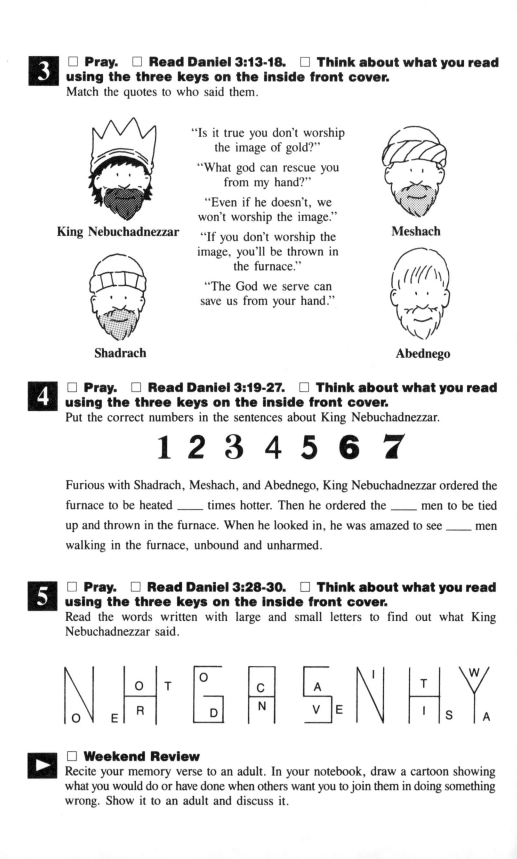

**King Nebuchadnezzar**

"Is it true you don't worship the image of gold?"

"What god can rescue you from my hand?"

"Even if he doesn't, we won't worship the image."

"If you don't worship the image, you'll be thrown in the furnace."

"The God we serve can save us from your hand."

**Meshach**

**Shadrach**

**Abednego**

**4** ☐ **Pray.** ☐ **Read Daniel 3:19-27.** ☐ **Think about what you read using the three keys on the inside front cover.**
Put the correct numbers in the sentences about King Nebuchadnezzar.

# 1 2 3 4 5 6 7

Furious with Shadrach, Meshach, and Abednego, King Nebuchadnezzar ordered the furnace to be heated _____ times hotter. Then he ordered the _____ men to be tied up and thrown in the furnace. When he looked in, he was amazed to see _____ men walking in the furnace, unbound and unharmed.

**5** ☐ **Pray.** ☐ **Read Daniel 3:28-30.** ☐ **Think about what you read using the three keys on the inside front cover.**
Read the words written with large and small letters to find out what King Nebuchadnezzar said.

▶ ☐ **Weekend Review**
Recite your memory verse to an adult. In your notebook, draw a cartoon showing what you would do or have done when others want you to join them in doing something wrong. Show it to an adult and discuss it.

**1** ☐ **Pray.** ☐ **Read Jonah 1:1-6.** ☐ **Think about what you read using the three keys on the inside front cover.**

Number the events in the correct order.

_____ God sent a violent storm.

_____ Jonah went to Joppa.

_____ The captain told Jonah to call on his god.

_____ Jonah went on a ship sailing for Tarshish.

_____ Jonah ran away from God.

_____ The sailors threw cargo overboard.

_____ The sailors were afraid and cried out to their gods.

_____ God told Jonah to preach in Ninevah.

_____ The captain woke Jonah from his deep sleep.

**2** ☐ **Pray.** ☐ **Read Jonah 1:7-12.** ☐ **Think about what you read using the three keys on the inside front cover.**

Put the quotes in the correct speech balloons.

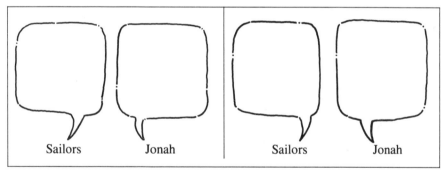

Sailors     Jonah          Sailors     Jonah

"I'm a Hebrew. I worship the Lord who made the sea and land."

"What should we do to you to make the sea calm down?"

"What do you do? Where are you from?"

"Throw me into the sea. The storm is my fault."

**3** ☐ **Pray.** ☐ **Read Jonah 1:13-17.** ☐ **Think about what you read using the three keys on the inside front cover.**

Use the code to find out what happened to Jonah after he was thrown into the sea.

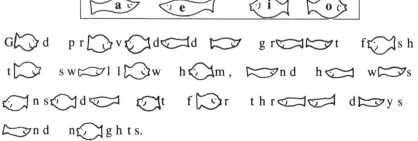

**4** ☐ **Pray.** ☐ **Read Jonah 2:1-6.** ☐ **Think about what you read using the three keys on the inside front cover.**

To see what Jonah said when he was in the fish, write every other letter. Go around the fish twice.

Start ⟶

Finish ⟶

_____
_____
_____
_____

**5** ☐ **Pray.** ☐ **Read Jonah 2:7-10.** ☐ **Think about what you read using the three keys on the inside front cover.**

Write the first letters of the objects to see what God told the fish to do.

▶ ☐ **Weekend Review**

Recite your memory verse to an adult. Think of groups of people who haven't heard God's Word. In your notebook, list three ways to help them, such as sending them Bibles or helping missionaries who translate the Bible for them.

## WEEK 48 ☐ Memorize: Jonah 3:10a

**1** ☐ **Pray.** ☐ **Read Jonah 3:1-5.** ☐ **Think about what you read using the three keys on the inside front cover.**

Shade in the boxes marked with squares. Then read the unshaded boxes to see what happened after Jonah preached.

| T | S | H | E | N | P | I | N | E | R | V | I |
|---|---|---|---|---|---|---|---|---|---|---|---|
| N | T | E | S | O | B | E | E | L | I | R | E |
| V | E | N | T | D | O | G | O | E | S | D | O |

**2** ☐ **Pray.** ☐ **Read Jonah 3:6-10.** ☐ **Think about what you read using the three keys on the inside front cover.**

Cross out the incorrect words to find out what happened in Ninevah.

When the **news/prophet** reached the king, he **rose/talked** from his throne, took off his royal **crown/robes,** put on **cotton/sackcloth,** and sat in the **dust/bath** to show he was very sad. He ordered, "All people and animals should neither **eat/play** nor **sleep/drink. All/Some** should put on **sackcloth/shoes. Some/Everyone** should call urgently on God and **stop/continue** their evil ways." When God **told/saw** what they **did/wanted** and how they turned from their **careful/evil** ways, he had **compassion/anger** and did not **destroy/help** them.

**3** ☐ Pray.   ☐ Read Jonah 4:1-4.   ☐ Think about what you read using the three keys on the inside front cover.

Fill in the letters to find out how Jonah felt when God did not destroy Ninevah.

## VERY DISPLEASED AND ANGRY

**4** ☐ Pray.   ☐ Read Jonah 4:5-8.   ☐ Think about what you read using the three keys on the inside front cover.

Draw what happened while Jonah sat watching the city of Ninevah.

**5** ☐ Pray.   ☐ Read Jonah 4:9-11.   ☐ Think about what you read using the three keys on the inside front cover.

Use the code to find out what God said to Jonah, who was angry when the vine died.

| 0 | 1 | 2 | 3 | 4 | 5 | 6 | 7 | 8 | 9 | 10 | 11 | 12 | 13 | 14 | 15 | 16 | 17 | 18 | 19 | 20 | 21 | 22 | 23 | 24 | 25 | 26 |
|---|---|---|---|---|---|---|---|---|---|----|----|----|----|----|----|----|----|----|----|----|----|----|----|----|----|----|
| space | a | b | c | d | e | f | g | h | i | j | k | l | m | n | o | p | q | r | s | t | u | v | w | x | y | z |

25 15 21 0 1 18 5 0 3 15 14 3 5 18 14 5 4 0 1 2 15 21 20 0 20 8 9 19 0

22 9 14 5 0 19 8 15 21 12 4 14 20 0 9 0 2 5 0 3 15 14 3 5 18 14 5 4 0

1 2 15 21 20 0 1 12 12 0 20 8 5 0 16 5 15 16 12 5 0 9 14 0 14 9 14 5 22 1 8 ?

▶ ☐ **Weekend Review**

Recite your memory verse to an adult. In your notebook, write a story of a modern Jonah. Read your story to a friend, and talk about how God worked with Jonah and the people of Ninevah.

**1** ☐ **Pray.** ☐ **Read 1 Timothy 2:1-7.** ☐ **Think about what you read using the three keys on the inside front cover.**
Use the code to find out what the apostle Paul said to do.

| A | E | F |
|---|---|---|
| L | O | P |
| R | Y | space |

_____

⌐⌐⌐⌐⌐⌐⌐⌐⌐⌐⌐⌐⌐⌐⌐⌐⌐⌐⌐⌐⌐

**2** ☐ **Pray.** ☐ **Read 1 Timothy 4:1-8.** ☐ **Think about what you read using the three keys on the inside front cover.**
Cross out all words starting with *N* to see what Paul said about training.

Never Train nobody yourself not to be neat godly next. No Physical nerve training has not some need value, but new godliness has note value for neither both the near present and the name life to nod come now.

**3** ☐ **Pray. Read 1 Timothy 4:9-16.** ☐ **Think about what you read using the three keys on the inside front cover.**
Unscramble the words to find out what Paul told Timothy.

Don't let anyone look down on you **acubsee** _____ you're young.

Be an **axlemep** _____ for the **livesreeb** _____ in the

way you live. Keep on reading the **putcrierss** _____ to people,

**carginhep** _____, and **getchain** _____.

**4** ☐ **Pray.** ☐ **Read 1 Timothy 6:3-10.** ☐ **Think about what you read using the three keys on the inside front cover.**
Match the keys to the keyholes. Starting with keyhole #1, read each keyhole and then its matching key to find out what Paul said about what is valuable.

But (1) with (2) is (3)

contentment    godliness    great gain

**5** ☐ **Pray.** ☐ **Read 1 Timothy 6:11-16.** ☐ **Think about what you read using the three keys on the inside front cover.**

Search for the words from Paul's command to Timothy.

```
A  P  P  E  A  R  I  N  G  H  E  C  N  A  R  U  D  N  E  T
E  L  S  S  E  N  E  L  T  N  E  G  H  E  M  I  T  O  P  S
U  S  E  T  A  B  R  I  G  H  T  E  O  U  S  N  E  S  S  T
S  E  T  E  R  N  A  L  L  I  F  E  A  S  E  D  N  V  D  E
R  A  C  O  N  F  E  S  S  I  O  N  E  W  E  L  T  W  O  E
U  T  H  R  O  Z  T  N  E  M  D  N  A  M  M  O  C  O  G  L
P  S  J  E  S  U  S  S  E  N  I  L  D  O  G  H  E  R  E  F
```

| | | | | | |
|---|---|---|---|---|---|
| flee | appearing | pursue | godliness | faith | love |
| God | time | hold | Jesus | eternal life | confession |
| commandment | righteousness | endurance | gentleness | | |

▶ ☐ **Weekend Review**

Recite your memory verse to an adult. Find out who the government officials in your community are and who your national government representatives are. List them in your notebook. Choose one official to pray for this week.

---

## WEEK 50 ☐ Memorize: James 4:10

**1** ☐ **Pray.** ☐ **Read James 3:1-12.** ☐ **Think about what you read using the three keys on the inside front cover.**

Circle the things James compares the tongue with.

| | | | | | | | | |
|---|---|---|---|---|---|---|---|---|
| wind | ship | bit | furnace | road | fire | water | horse | plow |
| steering wheel | ocean | spark | trumpet | salt | pepper | rudder | | |

**2** ☐ **Pray.** ☐ **Read James 3:13-18.** ☐ **Think about what you read using the three keys on the inside front cover.**

Mark the statements about wisdom either *true* or *false*.

\_\_\_\_ A wise person should show wisdom by living right.

\_\_\_\_ Wisdom from God is peace loving and considerate.

\_\_\_\_ A wise person should do good deeds with pride.

\_\_\_\_ You should boast about being envious and selfish.

\_\_\_\_ Wisdom from God is pure.

\_\_\_\_ Peacemakers receive a harvest of riches.

\_\_\_\_ Wisdom from God is not fair or honest.

\_\_\_\_ Where there is envy and selfishness, there is disorder and evil.

\_\_\_\_ Wisdom from God is merciful and sincere.

\_\_\_\_ Earthly "wisdom" is unspiritual.

## 3

☐ **Pray.** ☐ **Read James 4:1-6.** ☐ **Think about what you read using the three keys on the inside front cover.**

Do the math problems first. Then use the code to find out what James said.

| 1 | 2 | 3 | 4 | 5 | 6 | 7 | 8 | 9 | 10 | 11 | 12 | 13 | 14 | 15 |
|---|---|---|---|---|---|---|---|---|----|----|----|----|----|----|
| A | D | E | F | G | H | I | L | M | N | O | R | T | W | Y |

$$8-4 \quad 7+5 \quad 13-6 \quad 10-7 \quad 5+5 \quad 10-8 \qquad 6+5 \quad 10-6 \qquad 8+5 \quad 14-8 \quad 18-15$$

☐ ☐ ☐ ☐ ☐ ☐   ☐ ☐   ☐ ☐ ☐

___  ___  ___  ___  ___  ___   ___  ___   ___  ___  ___

$$9+5 \quad 21-10 \quad 7+5 \quad 12-4 \quad 27-25 \quad = \quad 19-16 \quad 20-10 \quad 14-11 \quad 6+3 \quad 8+7$$

☐ ☐ ☐ ☐ ☐   ☐ ☐ ☐ ☐ ☐

___  ___  ___  ___  ___   ___  ___  ___  ___  ___

$$4+7 \quad 19-15 \qquad 2+3 \quad 22-11 \quad 18-16$$

☐ ☐   ☐ ☐ ☐

___  ___   ___  ___  ___

☐ **Pray.** ☐ **Read James 4:7-12.** ☐ **Think about what you read using the three keys on the inside front cover.**

Go through the maze by following the things that James said to do.

| S T A R T | submit to God | resist the devil | look out for yourself | be sad about your sin | be humble before God | don't slander | F I N I S H |
|---|---|---|---|---|---|---|---|
| | watch other people | come near to God | clean sin from your life | purify your heart | don't care | don't judge | |

☐ **Pray.** ☐ **Read James 4:13-17.** ☐ **Think about what you read using the three keys on the inside front cover.**

To find out what James said, cross out the first letter in each group of letters. Then write the letters that are left, and separate them into words.

CANYONE  OWHOKN  TOW  ISTHER  NIGHT  STHI  ONGT  SODOB
CUT  ODOE  ASNO  ATDO  SITS  PINS

---

▶ ☐ **Weekend Review**

Recite your memory verse to an adult. In your notebook, list three ways to do good in your family, such as helping parents with chores or sharing with brothers or sisters. Choose one to do this week.

**1**   ☐ **Pray.**   ☐ **Read 1 John 1:1-4.**   ☐ **Think about what you read using the three keys on the inside front cover.**

Use the sounds of the objects to see what the apostle John said were his reasons for writing to believers.

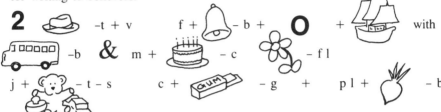

**2** 🎩 −t + v    f + 🔔 − b + **O** + ⛵ with
🚌 −b **&** m + 🎂 − c   🌼 − f l
j + 🧸 − t − s   c + [GUM] − g + p l + 🌱 − b

**2**   ☐ **Pray.**   ☐ **Read 1 John 1:5-10.**   ☐ **Think about what you read using the three keys on the inside front cover.**

To find out two things John said, read the darker words first and then the lighter ones.

**If** If **we** we **confess** walk **our** in **sins** the **he** light **is** as **faithful** he **and** is **just** in **and** the **will** light **forgive** we **us** have **our** fellowship **sins** with **and** each **purify** other **us**

**3**   ☐ **Pray.**   ☐ **Read 1 John 2:1-8.**   ☐ **Think about what you read using the three keys on the inside front cover.**

Follow the words through the maze to see what John said we should do.

```
      E D B R H  I V E I N X B T R S J E
Start W H W Q K L M P J G H K C W A Q S
      J O Z X B O T S L O D R G L K S U
      W E V E L F U M V Q M C Y A V D I
      L O Z R C L A I T X U S T W J F D
                                        Finish
```

**4**   ☐ **Pray.**   ☐ **Read 1 John 2:9-14.**   ☐ **Think about what you read using the three keys on the inside front cover.**

Shade in the squares marked with only one line to see what John said people who love others live in.

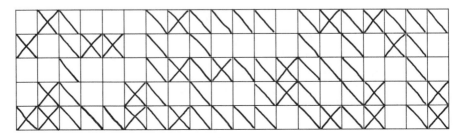

## 5

□ **Pray.** □ **Read 1 John 2:15-17.** □ **Think about what you read using the three keys on the inside front cover.**

Use the code to find out what John said really lasts.

| ① | ❶ | ② | ❷ | ③ | ❸ | ④ | ❹ | ⑤ | ❺ | ⑥ | ❻ | ⑦ | ❼ | ⑧ | ❽ | ⑨ | ❾ | ⑩ | ❿ | Ⓒ |
|---|---|---|---|---|---|---|---|---|---|---|---|---|---|---|---|---|---|---|---|---|
| a | b | d | e | f | g | h | i | l | m | n | o | p | r | s | t | u | v | w | y | space |

❽ ④ ❷ Ⓒ ⑩ ❻ ❼ ⑤ ❷ Ⓒ ① ⑥ ❷ Ⓒ ❷ ❾ ❷ ❼ ⑩ ❽ ④ ❹ ⑥ ❸ Ⓒ ⑦ ❷ ⑥ ⑦ ⑤ ❷ Ⓒ

⑩ ① ⑥ ❽ Ⓒ ③ ❼ ⑥ ⑤ Ⓒ ❹ ❽ Ⓒ ⑦ ① ❽ ❽ Ⓒ ① ⑩ ① ⑩ Ⓒ ❶ ⑨ ❽ Ⓒ ❽ ④ ❷ Ⓒ

⑦ ❷ ❼ ⑧ ❻ ⑥ Ⓒ ⑩ ④ ⑥ Ⓒ ② ⑥ ❷ ⑧ Ⓒ ⑩ ④ ① ⑧ Ⓒ ❸ ⑥ ② Ⓒ ⑩ ① ⑥ ❽ ⑧ Ⓒ

⑤ ❹ ❾ ❷ ⑧ Ⓒ ③ ⑥ ❼ ❷ ❾ ❷ ❼

## ▶ □ **Weekend Review**

Recite your memory verse to an adult. This week, make a plan to have fun with friends from church. Some suggestions are going on a bike ride or having a picnic. Write your plan in your notebook.

## WEEK 52 □ Memorize: Revelation 5:12

## 1

□ **Pray.** □ **Read Revelation 4:1-5.** □ **Think about what you read using the three keys on the inside front cover.**

Draw the vision of heaven that the apostle John saw.

## 2

□ **Pray.** □ **Read Revelation 4:6-11.** □ **Think about what you read using the three keys on the inside front cover.**

Write the missing letter of the alphabet on each line to find out what the four living creatures and 24 elders in John's vision of heaven did.

```
A B C D E F G H I J K L M N O P Q R S T U V X Y Z     _____
A B C D E F G H I J K L M N P Q R S T U V W X Y Z     _____
A B C D E F G H I J K L M N O P Q S T U V W X Y Z     _____
A B C D E F G H I J K L M N O P Q R T U V W X Y Z     _____
A B C D E F G I J K L M N O P Q R S T U V W X Y Z     _____
A B C D E F G H J K L M N O P Q R S T U V W X Y Z     _____
A B C D E F G H I J K L M N O Q R S T U V W X Y Z     _____
A B C D F G H I J K L M N O P Q R S T U V W X Y Z     _____
A B C E F G H I J K L M N O P Q R S T U V W X Y Z     _____
```

**3** ☐ **Pray.** ☐ **Read Revelation 5:1-5.** ☐ **Think about what you read using the three keys on the inside front cover.**

Shade in the spaces marked with dots to see who was able to open the scroll.

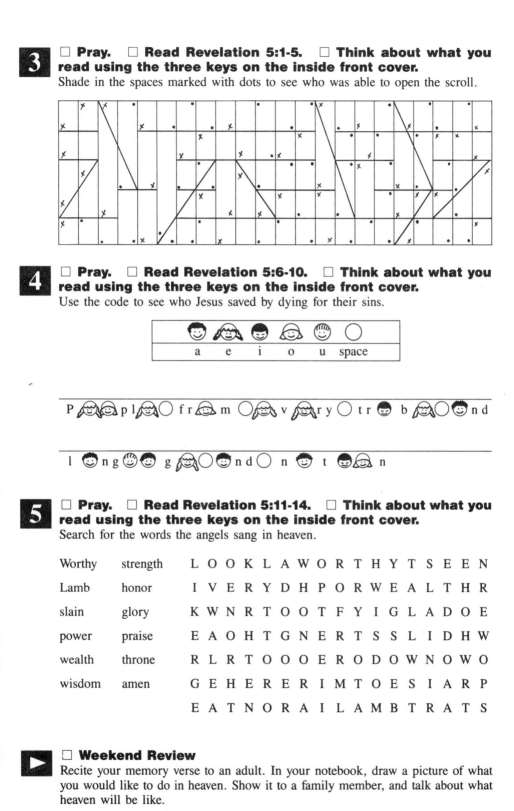

**4** ☐ **Pray.** ☐ **Read Revelation 5:6-10.** ☐ **Think about what you read using the three keys on the inside front cover.**

Use the code to see who Jesus saved by dying for their sins.

| 😊 | 👧 | 😊 | 👩 | 😄 | ○ |
|----|----|----|----|----|----|
| a | e | i | o | u | space |

P e o p l e  f r o m  e v e r y  t r i b e  a n d

l a n g u a g e  a n d  n a t i o n

**5** ☐ **Pray.** ☐ **Read Revelation 5:11-14.** ☐ **Think about what you read using the three keys on the inside front cover.**

Search for the words the angels sang in heaven.

| Worthy | strength |
| Lamb | honor |
| slain | glory |
| power | praise |
| wealth | throne |
| wisdom | amen |

```
L O O K L A W O R T H Y T S E E N
I V E R Y D H P O R W E A L T H R
K W N R T O O T F Y I G L A D O E
E A O H T G N E R T S S L I D H W
R L R T O O O E R O D O W N O W O
G E H E R E R I M T O E S I A R P
E A T N O R A I L A M B T R A T S
```

▶ ☐ **Weekend Review**

Recite your memory verse to an adult. In your notebook, draw a picture of what you would like to do in heaven. Show it to a family member, and talk about what heaven will be like.